養生家常菜

Chinese Home Cooking
for Health

作　　　者　　　林麗華

翻　　　譯　　　葛潔輝

翻 譯 顧 問　　　何久恩

出　版　者　　　純青出版社有限公司

　　　　　　　　台北市松江路125號5樓

　　　　　　　　郵政劃撥12106299

　　　　　　　　電話：(02)25084331　傳真：(02)25074902

著作財產權人　　財團法人味全文化教育基金會

版 權 所 有　　　局版台業字第3884號

　　　　　　　　中華民國86年12月初版發行

印　　　刷　　　中華彩色印刷股份有限公司

定　　　價　　　新台幣參佰元整

Author　　　　　　　Lee Hwa Lin

Translator　　　　　　Connie Wolhardt

Translation Consultant　John Holt

Publisher　　　　　　Chin Chin Publishing Co., Ltd.
　　　　　　　　　　　5th fl., 125, Sung Chiang Rd,
　　　　　　　　　　　Taipei, Taiwan, R.O.C.
　　　　　　　　　　　Tel:(02)25084331 , Fax:(02)25074902

Distributor　　　　　　Wei-Chuan Publishing
　　　　　　　　　　　1455 Monterey Pass Rd., #110
　　　　　　　　　　　Monterey Park, CA 91754, U.S.A.
　　　　　　　　　　　Tel:(213)2613880 . 2613878
　　　　　　　　　　　Fax:(213)2613299

Printer　　　　　　　China Color Printing Co., Inc.
　　　　　　　　　　　Printed in Taiwan, R.O.C.

Copyright Holder　　　Copyright © 1998
　　　　　　　　　　　By Wei-Chuan Cultural Educational
　　　　　　　　　　　Foundation
　　　　　　　　　　　First Printing, Mar., 1998
　　　　　　　　　　　ISBN 0-941676-75-7

序

現代人生活的節奏太快，工作的壓力太大，罹患高血壓、糖尿病、血脂過高等現代病的人也愈來愈多，之所以會百病叢生，就其原因多半是不良的生活習慣與飲食作祟。

我們的身體就像一部機器，平時就需要保養，而均衡飲食就是保養機器的基本原則。每種食物都有它的特性及主要包含的維生素成分，因此，需要攝取不同的食物，使它們能在體內發揮不同的功能，同時，依照身體的需求來選擇烹調食物的方法，更可使健康事半功倍。

本書中每道食譜除了選用各種材料烹飪出色香味俱全的菜餚外，並列出它們的功效，讀者可依個人所需，來選擇適合自己的食物及烹飪方法。為了避免蔬菜上的殘餘農藥有害健康，本書特別增加生機篇，帶領讀者利用最簡易的空間，自行培養生機蔬菜；再用最原始的技巧去享受其中的美味。

這本食譜集結了八十道養生家常菜，特別感謝長庚聯合中醫診所張景琛醫師對每道菜的功效做專業性的指導與最後審核，使這本書在實用之餘，更具食療參考的附加價值。

Foreword

With the development of the modern science, many new diseases have been identified. They are finding more and more hypertension, diabetes and high cholesterol. Basically many of those diseases stem from unsound living and poor eating habits.

For good health, balanced meals are very important. Each food has its own unique property and provides different vitamins and minerals to serve the body. It is, therefore, important to choose and prepare proper meals to satisfy our needs.

The human body is like a machine, needing constant good maintenance. Every recipe in this book offers a tasty treat with a beautiful presentation. At the same time, each also lists beneficial functions so readers may choose meals most suitable to them. To avoid the harmful effects of agricultural pesticides, the organic chapter teaches readers the easiest methods for organic farming and cooking.

We would also like to thank Dr. Gean Tseng Chang for his professional direction and the final review.

Lee Hwa Lin

目錄 · Contents

生機類 · Organic

海鮮類 · Seafood

雞肉類 · Chicken

主食類 · Rice

羹湯類 · Soup

量器的介紹 ▪ Conversion Table

1 杯 = 236 c.c.
1 cup = 1C. = 236 c.c.

1 大匙 = 1湯匙 = 15 c.c.
1 Tablespoon = 1T. = 15 c.c.

1 小匙 = 1茶匙 = 5 c.c.
1 Teaspoon = 1t. = 5 c.c.

重量的換算 ▪ Measurement Equivalents

28 公克 = 28 g = 1 oz.

85 公克 = 85 g = 3 oz.

170公克 =170 g = 6 oz.

2 兩 = 75公克 = 75 g = $2\frac{1}{2}$ oz.

3 兩 = 115公克 = 115 g = $\frac{1}{4}$ lb.

4 兩 = 150公克 = 150 g = $\frac{1}{3}$ lb.

6 兩 = 225公克 = 225 g = $\frac{1}{2}$ lb.

8 兩 = 300公克 = 300 g = $\frac{2}{3}$ lb.

9 兩 = 340公克 = 340 g = $\frac{3}{4}$ lb.

12兩 = 450公克 = 450 g = 1 lb.

16兩 = 600公克 = 600 g = $1\frac{1}{3}$ lb. = 1 斤

lb. = pound   g = gram   oz. = ounce

材料的前處理 ....

海參的發法 · Dried Sea Cucumber

1 乾海參洗淨,泡水1天,隔天換水,煮開後熄火,待水涼後換水再煮,如此1天3次,連續發3天至軟。

1 Wash the dried sea cucumber, soak in water for one day, place the sea cucumber into new water and bring the water to a boil. When the water is cooled, change again to new water; bring to another boil. Repeat the process 3 times a day for 2 days, until the sea cucumber turns soft.

1

苦瓜的處理 · Bitter Melon Preparation

1 苦瓜洗淨。
2 直切成兩半,刮去瓜囊及內膜。
3 切片或切塊。

1 Wash the bitter melon.
2 Cut into halves lengthwise. Scoop out seeds and inner films.
3 Slice or cut into serving pieces.

1

2

3

蔥段的切法 · Green Onion Sections

1 蔥洗淨。
2 去頭、尾部份。
3 再切成3公分長段。

1 Wash the green onion.
2 Trim off the tops and roots.
3 Cut into 1 $\frac{1}{4}$" (3 cm) long sections.

1

2

3

薑片的切法 · Ginger Slices

1 薑洗淨，去皮。
2 斜切成 1.5 × 2.5 公分之片狀。

1 Wash the ginger and pare off the skin.
2 Cut into $5/_8$" x 1" (1.5 x 2.5 cm) diagonal slices.

1

2

川燙 · Parboil

1 一鍋水以大火煮開。
2 放入材料再煮開，隨即撈起。
3 漂冷水。

1 Bring water to a boil over high heat.
2 Add materials and bring to a boil once again.
3 Rinse under cold water.

1

2

3

高湯的製作 · Stock

1 以豬、牛、雞的肉或骨頭入開水中川燙。
2 再將肉或骨頭取出洗淨。
3 另一鍋水煮開，再入洗淨的肉或骨頭，加少許蔥、薑、
　酒慢火熬煮出來的湯，謂之高湯。

1 Parboil pork, beef, chicken or bones.
2 Remove from wok and wash.
3 Bring new clean water to a boil, add the meat or
　the bones together with some green onion,
　ginger, and cooking wine. Simmer over low heat
　until the soup is tasty.

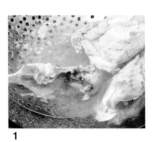
1

2

3

綠豆芽 · Mung Bean Sprouts

綠豆 ¹/₂杯
塑膠籃（25×20×6公分）1個
紗布（25×40公分）1塊

$^1/_2$ C. mung beans
1 plastic basket, 10" x 8" x 2 $^1/_4$" (
25 x 20 x 6 cm)
1 gauze cloth, 10" x 16" (25 x 40 cm)

1 紗布洗淨，對摺成25×20公分大小，鋪於塑膠籃底部備用（圖一）。

2 綠豆洗淨，加水浸泡至皮稍裂（約10－12小時），瀝乾鋪於塑膠籃內（圖二），置暗處或加蓋，每天早晚各澆水1次。

3 豆芽長至2.5－4公分長時（約3－5天），即可採收。

■ 1 黃豆、紅豆、黑豆等亦可以此方法培育。
　2 利用簡便容器，如不銹鋼水壺。種子量以不超過容器體積的十分之一為準。

1 Wash gauze cloth and fold into halves 10" x 8" (25 x 20 cm). Line the gauze cloth at the bottom of the plastic basket (illus. 1)

2 Rinse mung beans and soak in water until the outer coats are slightly cracked (about 10 to 12 hours). Drain. Spread the beans in the basket (illus. 2). Place the basket at a dark place or cover. Water twice a day, every morning and evening.

3 When the sprouts are 1" to 1 $^1/_2$" (2.5 to 4 cm) tall (about 3 to 5 days). They are ready for harvest.

■ 1 Same method for soy bean sprouts, red bean sprouts, and black bean sprouts.
　2 For easy method: any container may be used, i.e. stainless water kettles etc. as long as the seeds do not exceed ten percent of the container.

苜蓿芽 · Alfalfa Sprouts

苜蓿種子（圖一）4大匙
塑膠籃（25×20×6公分）1個
紗布（25×40公分）1塊

4 T. alfalfa seeds (illus. 1)
1 plastic basket, 10" x 8" x 2 $^1/_2$" (
25 x 20 x 6 cm)
1 gauze cloth, 10" x 16" (25 x 40 cm)

1 紗布洗淨，對摺成25×20公分大小，鋪於塑膠籃底部。

2 苜蓿種子洗淨，加水浸泡至皮稍裂（約4－6小時），鋪於塑膠籃內（圖一），置暗處或加蓋（圖二），每天早晚各澆水1次（天氣太熱可放於冰箱下層培育）。

3 當豆芽長到2.5－4公分長（約3－5天）（圖三），放至明亮處或掀去蓋子，見光 $^1/_2$－1天，稍綠化即可採收。

■ 蘿蔔芽、豌豆芽等培育方法與苜蓿芽相同，但種子浸泡需延長至7－12小時。

1 Wash gauze cloth, fold to half size 10" x 8" (25 x 20 cm), and line it at the bottom of the plastic basket.

2 Rinse alfalfa seeds, soak in water until the outer coats are slightly cracked (about 4 to 6 hours). Spread the seeds in the basket (illus. 1). Place the basket at a dark place or cover (illus. 2). Sprinkle on water twice a day, in the morning and evening. (If the weather is too hot, place on the lower shelf of a refrigerator).

3 When the sprouts grow to be 1" to 1 $^1/_2$" (2.5 to 4 cm) tall (about 3 to 5 days), (illus. 3) Move the basket to a bright location or remove the lid. The sprouts are ready for harvest, after $^1/_2$ to 1 day.

■ Same method for turnip sprouts, and sweet pea sprouts. But the seeds need to be soaked for 7 to 12 hours.

小麥草 · Wheat Grass

小麥 $^1/_2$ 杯
淺盤（２５×２０×３公分）２個
塑膠籃（２５×２０×６公分）１個
紗布（２５×２０公分）１塊
有機介質５杯

$^1/_2$ C. wheat seeds
2 shallow trays, 10" x 8" x 1 $^1/_4$"
(25 x 20 x 3 cm)
1 plastic basket, 10' x 8" x 2 $^1/_2$"
(25 x 20 x 6 cm)
1 gauze cloth, 10" x 8" (25 x
20 cm)
5 C. organic medium

1

2

3

1 紗布鋪於塑膠籃內備用。

2 小麥種子洗淨，去除破損種子及雜質，加水浸泡約８－１０小時，瀝乾，平鋪於
塑膠籃內，再將另一淺盤蓋於其上（圖一），直到發芽（約１ $^1/_2$ 天）。其間需噴
水１－２次，以保持種子的陰濕狀態，即為催芽過程。

3 有機介質平鋪於一淺盤上（約２.５公分厚），將催過芽的小麥平鋪於有機介質上
（圖二），再將空淺盤倒蓋在上面，待小麥芽長至約１.５公分高（約２－３天）。
掀開淺盤讓小麥芽見光（約３－４天），培植期間每天早晚各噴水１次，但勿噴
灑過多以免種子浸爛。

4 當小麥草長到１２－１５公分高（圖三）（共約７－１０天），即可收割。

1 Line the gauze at the bottom of the plastic basket.

2 Rinse wheat seeds, discard the dregs and damaged seeds. Soak in water for
8 to 10 hours. Drain and spread the seeds in the plastic basket. Put a
shallow tray on top (illus. 1) until germinating (about 1 $^1/_2$ days). During
the period, spray with water 1 or 2 times to keep the seeds moist.

3 Spread the organic medium on a tray (about 1 " or 2.5 cm thick), place a
layer of germinated seeds on the organic medium (illus. 2). Invert the other
tray and cover the organic medium tray until the sprouts reach $^5/_8$ " (1.5
cm) tall (about 2 to 3 days). Remove the inverted tray to let the light in
(about 3 to 4 days). Spray with water every morning and evening. Do not
over water, the seeds may rot.

4 When sprouts reach 4 $^3/_4$ " to 6" (12 to 15 cm) tall (illus. 3), (totaling 7 to
10 days). They are ready for harvest.

生機沙拉 · Organic Salad Platter

枸杞子 .... 2 大匙

1 ┌ 苜蓿芽 .... 3 杯
  │ 綠豆芽 .... 1 杯
  │ 蘿蔔芽、豌豆芽 ....
  └ .... 各 3 大匙

2 ┌ 小黃瓜 .... 8 5 公克
  │ 紫菜 .... 1 張
  │ 冷開水 .... 2 大匙
  │ 黑糖 .... 1 大匙
  │ 檸檬汁 ... 1 ¹/₂ 小匙
  └ 純麻油 .... 1 小匙

2 T. ..... lycium berries
1 ┌ 3 C. alfalfa sprouts
  │ 1 C. bean sprouts
  │ 3 T. each: turnip
  │ sprouts, Chinese
  └ snow pea sprouts

2 ┌ 3 oz. (85 g) ....
  │ gherkin cucumbers
  │ 1 .... nori sheet
  │ 2 T. .... water
  │ 1 T. ..... dark brown
  │ sugar
  │ 1 ¹/₂ t . lemon juice
  └ 1 t . pure sesame oil

1 枸杞子以冷開水稍沖洗，瀝乾；**1** 料漂洗去殼，亦以冷開水稍沖洗，瀝乾；小黃瓜洗淨切碎；紫菜撕碎備用。

2 **2** 料入果汁機內以中速攪拌 3 0 秒（勿太細碎），即為黃瓜醬。

3 **1** 料置盤上，撒上枸杞子，再淋上黃瓜醬即可。

功效：營養豐富、清爽可口，多食可活化身體機能、改善虛弱體質。

1 Rinse lycium berries and drain. Rinse all ingredients in **1** and remove the bean shells. Wash gherkin cucumbers and chop fine. Tear nori sheet to fine.

2 Puree **2** in blender for 30 seconds at medium speed (not too fine) for cucumber dressing.

3 Place **1** on a plate, sprinkle on lycium berries and pour on the cucumber dressing. Serve.

Functions: Nutritious, light and tasty. Frequent intake may improve metabolism, strengthen body functions.

苜蓿手捲 · Alfalfa Rolls

生菜 .... 6 片	苜蓿芽 .... 3 杯	**6 leaves** .... **lettuce**	**3 C.** ..... **alfalfa sprouts**
沙拉醬 .... 4 大匙	蘿蔔芽 .... 3 大匙	**4 T.** .... **mayonnaise**	**3 T.** ...... **turnip spouts**
紫菜 .... 3 張		**3** .... **nori sheets**	

1 生菜洗淨，拭乾水份；苜蓿芽、蘿蔔芽分別洗淨，以冷開水稍沖洗後瀝乾，再均分成 6 等份。

2 紫菜每張分成兩小張，入烤箱內稍烤或置已燒熱的鍋中烘一下，使紫菜香脆。

3 每一張紫菜攤平，鋪上 1 片生菜，1 份苜蓿芽，淋上 2 小匙沙拉醬，再鋪上 1 份蘿蔔芽，最後捲成甜筒狀。

功效：清淡而營養，可清血脂、降血壓和健胃整腸。

1 Wash lettuce and pat dry. Rinse both sprouts, drain and divide into 6 equal portions.

2 Cut each nori sheet into halves, roast in oven or heated wok for a while to crisp.

3 On each nori sheet, place a lettuce leaf, a portion of alfalfa sprouts, and 2 t. mayonnaise. Then place a portion of turnip sprouts. Roll it up as a cylinder. Serve.

Functions: Light and nutritious. May improve cholesterol, blood pressure and digestive organs.

胡蘿蔔麥草汁 · Carrot and Wheat Grass Punch

小麥草 .... 10公克　　蜂蜜 2小匙

胡蘿蔔（淨重）...... 5公克

1 小麥草以冷開水稍沖洗；胡蘿蔔切碎備用。

2 果汁機內入小麥草、胡蘿蔔及冰開水1杯，以中速打碎約2分鐘，去渣，加蜂蜜即可。

　功效：含有豐富的維他命A、B、E，有清血、美容、抗癌、大補元氣之功效。

$^1/_3$ oz. (10 g) wheat grass　　2 t. .... honey

$^1/_6$ oz. (5 g) ...... carrot

(net weight)

1 Rinse wheat grass. Chop carrot.

2 Puree wheat grass, carrot and 1 C. ice water at medium speed for 2 minutes in a blender. Discard the dregs. Mix in honey and serve.

Functions: Rich in vitamin A, B, and E. May cleanse blood and improve immunity. May promote physical beauty.

麥乳汁 · Oatmeal Milk

小麥草 .... 1 0公克　　蜂蜜 .... 2 小匙
即食燕麥片 .... 3 大匙

1 小麥草以冷開水稍沖洗備用。

2 果汁機內入小麥草及冰開水¹/₄杯，以中速打碎約2分
  鐘，去渣，麥草汁留用。

3 燕麥片加熱開水¹/₄杯拌成糊狀，待涼，置果汁機內，
  加冰開水¹/₂杯稍攪拌（約20秒），倒出與麥草汁及
  蜂蜜拌勻即可。

  功效：有整腸健胃之功效，常食能預防疾病。

$^1/_3$ oz. (10 g)　**wheat grass**　　2 t. .... **honey**
3 T. .... **instant oatmeal**

1　Rinse wheat grass.

2　Puree wheat grass and $^1/_4$ C. ice water at medium
   speed for 2 minutes in a blender. Discard the dregs.

3　Add $^1/_4$ C. hot water into the oatmeal and mix into
   a paste; leave to cool. Puree the oatmeal and $^1/_2$ C.
   ice water for 20 seconds in a blender. Mix it well
   with wheat grass juice and honey. Serve.

   Functions: May improve digestive functions and
   immunity.

番茄烤鮭魚 · Baked Salmon

鮭魚 ... 8兩（３００公克）
番茄 １８５公克
九層塔葉 .... ¹/₄ 杯
奶油 ２大匙
紅蔥頭末 １大匙

1 [白葡萄酒 １大匙
　　 鹽、黑胡椒粉各１小匙

2 [白葡萄酒 １大匙
　　 鹽、糖 各１小匙

²/₃ lb. (300 g)...salmon
steak
6 ¹/₂ oz. (185 g) tomatoes
¹/₄ C. fresh basil leaves
2 T. .... butter
1 T. minced red shallots

1 [1 T. white wine
　　 1 t. each: salt, black
　　 pepper powder

2 [1 T. white wine
　　 1 t. each: sugar, salt

1　鮭魚洗淨拭乾，入**1**料拌醃；番茄洗淨，底部劃十字，入開水中燙至皮掀起，撈起漂涼，去皮切開去籽，再切１平方公分寬之小丁；九層塔葉洗淨；烤箱預熱至２００℃。

2　鍋熱入奶油２大匙燒熱，入紅蔥頭炒香，續入番茄炒勻，再入**2**料及九層塔葉拌勻備用。

3　烤盤上置１０×１２公分鋁箔紙１張，入鮭魚，再將炒好之番茄置於鮭魚上，入烤箱烤至魚熟（約１２分鐘）。
功效：有整腸和淨血之功效，能幫助消化、降低體內膽固醇和防止便秘。

1　Wash and pat dry salmon, marinate in **1**. Wash tomatoes and score a cross at each bottom, scald in boiling water until the skin curls up. Remove the tomato skins and seeds, cut into ¹/₂" (1 cm) cubes. Wash fresh basil leaves. Preheat the oven to 400°F (200°C).

2　Heat a wok, add 2 T. butter and heat. Stir-fry minced shallots until fragrant. Add tomatoes to fry. Mix in **2** and basil leaves.

3　Line a baking sheet with 4" x 4 ³/₄" (10 x 12 cm) foil paper. Place the salmon on the baking sheet. Spread a layer of tomato mixture and bake until tender (about 12 minutes). Serve.

Function: May promote digestion. May lower cholesterol and prevent constipation.

樹子蒸鱈魚 · Steamed Cod

鱈魚（1片）.................. .... 9兩（340公克）	
蔥花 .... 1 大匙	
味精 .... $^1/_8$ 小匙	

1┤ 薑 .... 3 片
樹子、樹子醃汁 ....
.... 各 1 $^1/_2$ 大匙

$^3/_4$ lb. (340 g) ...... cod
1 T. .... chopped green onion

1┤ 3 slices ginger root
1 $^1/_2$ T. each: se-
bastan plum cordia,
sebastan plum cor-
dia juice

1 鱈魚洗淨，入**1**料醃20分鐘後入蒸鍋蒸15分鐘，蒸汁倒出留用，再撒上蔥花備用。

2 鍋熱入油1大匙燒熱，淋在蔥花上，蒸汁倒回鍋內，加味精調味，再淋回蔥花上即可。

■ 樹子可以梅子代替。

功效：清香開胃，有降血脂、解毒散腫、抗癌之功效。

1 Wash cod, marinate with **1** for 20 minutes. Steam for 15 minutes. Pour steamed fish juice in a bowl for later use. Sprinkle on chopped green onion.

2 Heat a wok, add 1 T. oil and heat. Pour the hot oil over the green onion. Pour the steamed fish juice over the green onion. Serve.

■ Sebastan plum cordia may be replace by preserved plumes.

Functions: Fruity and appetizing. May lower cholesterol and reduce edema. May protect against cancer.

韭黃炒鱈魚 · Cod and Chives

韭黃、鱈魚 ....
.... 各6兩（225公克）

1
┌ 薑............................ 4 片
│ 酒................... $^1/_2$ 大匙
│ 醬油 .... 1 小匙
└ 胡椒粉 .... $^1/_8$ 小匙

麵粉 .... 2 大匙

2
┌ 水 .... 1 大匙
│ 鹽 .... $^3/_8$ 小匙
│ 味精 .... $^1/_4$ 小匙
└ 胡椒粉 .... $^1/_8$ 小匙

1 鱈魚冰凍至稍硬，取出切4公分長條狀，入**1**料拌醃，待炸時再沾麵粉；韭黃洗淨，切3公分長段備用。

2 鍋熱入油3杯燒至七分熱（160℃），入魚條以大火炸至金黃色，撈起瀝油。

3 鍋內留油2大匙燒熱，入韭黃炒數下，續入**2**料炒勻，取出盛盤，再將炸好之魚條置於其上，食時拌勻即可。

功效：含有豐富的維他命Ｂ1，能增進食慾、殺菌整腸、消除疲勞，常食可預防感冒。

$^1/_2$ lb. (225 g) each: cod, Chinese yellow chives

1
┌ 4 slices ginger root
│ $^1/_2$ T. cooking wine
│ 1 t. soy sauce
└ $^1/_8$ t. pepper

2 T. .... flour

2
┌ 1 T. water
│ $^3/_8$ t. salt
└ $^1/_8$ t. pepper

1 Freeze the cod until slightly hard for easier handling. Cut the cod into $1^1/_2$" (4 cm) long strips and marinate in **1**. Dredge in flour prior to cooking. Wash Chinese yellow chives and cut into $1^1/_4$" (3 cm) sections.

2 Heat a wok, add 3 C. oil and heat to 325°F (160°C). Deep-fry cod strips until golden brown. Remove and drain off the oil.

3 Retain 2 T. oil in the wok and heat. Stir-fry Chinese yellow chives slightly. Add **2** to mix well. Remove to a plate. Arrange the cod strips on top of the yellow chives. Mix well before serving.

Functions: Rich in vitamin B1. May improve appetite. May reduce fatigue. Frequent intake may prevent catching cold.

韭黃蛤蜊肉 · Clams and Chives

蛤蜊 .. 1斤（６００公克）
韭黃 .. 8兩（３００公克）
辣椒絲 .... 1 大匙
薑末 .... 1 小匙

1
紹興酒 .... 1 小匙
鹽 .... $^1/_2$ 小匙
味精 .... $^1/_8$ 小匙

1 $^1/_3$ lb. (600 g)...clams
$^2/_3$ lb. (300g) ...Chinese
yellow chives
1 T. .... shredded
red chili pepper
1 t. minced ginger root

1
1 t. Shao Hsing rice
wine
$^1/_2$ t. salt

1 蛤蜊泡水吐沙洗淨，入開水中川燙至殼稍打開，熄火續
   燜２分鐘，撈起待涼，去殼取肉；韭黃洗淨切３公分
   長段備用。

2 鍋熱入油２大匙燒熱，入薑末爆香，續入韭黃炒數下，
   再入蛤蜊肉、**1**料及辣椒絲炒勻即可。

   功效：含有豐富的維他命Ａ、Ｂ、Ｃ和蛋白質，味道十
   分鮮美，具有健胃、補元氣，增加血液循環之功效。

1 Soak the clams in fresh water until all the sand is
   released then wash, cook in boiling water until
   opened. Turn off the heat and leave in water for 2
   minutes. Remove and leave to cool. Remove the
   clam meat. Wash Chinese yellow chives and cut
   into 1 $^1/_4$" (3 cm) sections.

2 Heat a wok, add 2 T. oil and heat. Stir-fry minced
   ginger root until fragrant. Add yellow chives and
   stir-fry a while. Add clam meat, **1** and shredded
   red chili pepper. Mix well and serve.

   Functions: Rich in vitamin A, B, C, and protein.
   Delicious and may improve blood circulation.

19

韭菜花炒墨魚 · Flowery Cuttlefish

墨魚 ... 6兩（225公克）
韭菜花4兩（150公克）
濕木耳 56公克
薑絲 .... $^1/_2$大匙

1
水 .... 2 大匙
酒 .... 1 大匙
鹽 .... $^1/_2$ 小匙
味精 .... $^1/_8$ 小匙

$^1/_2$ lb. (225 g) cuttlefish
$^1/_3$ lb. (150 g) chive buds
2 oz. (56 g) ..... soaked black wood ears
$^1/_2$ T. shredded ginger roots

1
2 T. water
1 T. cooking wine
$^1/_2$ t. salt

1 墨魚洗淨，內面切花刀，再切1×3.5公分片狀；韭菜花洗淨切3.5公分長段；木耳洗淨去蒂，切寬條。

2 鍋熱入油3大匙燒熱，入薑絲爆香，續入墨魚及木耳炒勻，再入韭菜花及**1**料炒至墨魚熟透。

功效：具有補血通經、促進荷爾蒙分泌及抗菌之功效。

1 Wash the cuttlefish, score diamonds on the inner surface; then cut into $^1/_2$" x 1 $^3/_8$" (1 x 3.5 cm) slices. Wash chive buds and cut into 1 $^3/_8$" (3.5 cm) sections. Wash soaked black wood ears, discard the stems and cut into thick strips.

2 Heat a wok, add 3 T. oil and heat. Stir-fry shredded ginger roots until fragrant. Add cuttlefish and soaked black wood ears, mix well. Add chive buds and **1**. Stir-fry until cuttlefish is tender. Serve.

Functions: May replenish the blood and promote hormone production.

珍珠蝦仁 · Shrimp and Corn

玉米罐頭（1罐）............
.... 8兩（３００公克）
蝦仁 ... 6兩（２２５公克）
辣椒 .... 1 條
蔥末 .... 3 大匙

1
┌ 酒 .... $^1/_2$ 大匙
│ 太白粉 .... 2 小匙
└ 鹽 .... $^1/_8$ 小匙

2
┌ 酒 .... 1 大匙
│ 粗黑胡椒粉 ... $^1/_2$ 小匙
└ 鹽、味精 .. 各 $^1/_8$ 小匙

$^2/_3$ lb. (300 g)...... 1 can whole kernel sweet corn
$^1/_2$ lb. (225 g)....shelled shrimp
1 ...... red chili pepper
3 T. ...minced green onion

1
┌ $^1/_2$ T. cooking wine
│ 2 t. cornstarch
└ $^1/_8$ t. salt

2
┌ 1 T. cooking wine
│ $^1/_2$ t. black pepper powder
└ $^1/_8$ t. salt

1 蝦仁去腸泥洗淨，拭乾水份，入**1**料拌醃；辣椒洗淨，切圓圈狀去籽備用。

2 鍋熱入油2大匙燒熱，入蔥末1大匙爆香，續入蝦仁炒至變色，再入玉米粒及**2**料炒勻，最後入辣椒圈及蔥末2大匙拌勻即可。

功效：為高蛋白、低脂肪適合全家食用的營養佳餚，有治療貧血、低血壓及增強體力之功效。

1 Remove the black veins and wash the shrimp; pat dry. Marinate with **1**. Wash red chili pepper and cut into rings; remove the seeds.

2 Heat a wok, add 2 T. oil and heat. Stir-fry 1 T. minced green onion until fragrant. Add shrimp and stir-fry until shrimp changes color. Mix in corn and **2**; stir well. Add chili rings and 2 T. minced green onions. Mix well and serve.

Functions: High in protein and low in fat, an ideal dish for whole family. May decrease anaemia, lower blood pressure.

蔬燴海參 · Sea Cucumber and Vegetables

烏參 8 兩（３００公克）　　熟筍片 ４５公克
濕木耳 .... ５６公克　　胡蘿蔔片、豌豆莢各２８公克

1
┌ 蔥 .... 5 段
├ 薑 .... 4 片
├ 水 .... 4 杯
└ 酒 .... 1 大匙

3
┌ 高湯 .... $^3/_4$ 杯
├ 醬油 .... 1 大匙
├ 麻油 .... 1 小匙
├ 鹽、糖 .... 各$^1/_2$ 小匙
└ 味精 .... $^1/_4$ 小匙

2
┌ 蔥 .... 6 段
└ 薑 .... 4 片

4
┌ 水 .... 1 大匙
└ 太白粉 .... $^3/_4$ 小匙

$^2/_3$ lb. (300 g) sea cucumber
2 oz. (56 g) soaked black wood ears

$1^1/_2$ oz. (45 g) ... boiled sliced bamboo shoots
1 oz. (28 g) each: carrot slices, Chinese snow peas

1
┌ 5 sections green onion
├ 4 slices ginger root
├ 4 C. water
└ 1 T. cooking wine

3
┌ $^3/_4$ C. stock
├ 1 T. soy sauce
├ 1 t. sesame oil
└ $^1/_2$ t. each: sugar, salt

2
┌ 6 sections green onion
└ 4 slices ginger root

4
┌ 1 T. water
└ $^3/_4$ t. cornstarch

1 烏參剖開去內臟，洗淨切厚片；木耳洗淨去蒂切片；豌豆莢去老纖維，洗淨備用。

2 鍋入**1**料煮開，續入烏參煮 2 分鐘，撈起漂涼瀝乾。

3 鍋熱入油 1 $^1/_2$ 大匙燒熱，入**2**料爆香，續入烏參、胡蘿蔔片、筍片、木耳炒勻，再入**3**料煮開，改小火煮約 5 分鐘，最後入豌豆莢拌勻並以**4**料勾芡即可。

功效：能預防高血壓及甲狀腺腫大，另有幫助發育，增強精力之功效。

1 Snip open the sea cucumber and remove the offal; wash and cut into thick slices. Wash black wood ears, discard the stems and slice. Remove the tough fibers on Chinese snow peas and wash.

2 Bring **1** to a boil. Add sea cucumber slices to cook for 2 minutes. Remove and rinse under cold water to cool; drain.

3 Heat a wok, add 1 $^1/_2$ T. oil and heat. Stir-fry **2** until fragrant. Add sea cucumber slices, carrot, bamboo shoots and wood ears to fry. Pour in **3** and bring to a boil. Simmer over low heat for 5 minutes. Mix in Chinese snow peas and thicken with **4**. Serve.

Functions: May prevent high blood pressure and swollen thyroid. May promote physical development and improve energy.

茄子烏參 · Sea Cucumber and Eggplant

烏參 .. 8兩（300公克）	薑 .... 4 片
茄子 250公克	蒜葉絲 .... $1/4$ 杯
蔥 .... 4 段	麻油 .... $1/2$ 小匙

1
| 蔥 .... 5 段 |
| 薑 .... 4 片 |
| 水 .... 4 杯 |
| 酒 .... 1 大匙 |

2
| 醬油 .... 2 大匙 |
| 酒 .... $1/2$ 大匙 |
| 糖 .... $1/2$ 小匙 |
| 味精、胡椒粉各 $1/8$ 小匙 |

3
| 水 .... 1 小匙 |
| 太白粉 .... $1/2$ 小匙 |

1 烏參去內臟洗淨，直切成兩半，再斜切長條狀；茄子洗淨去皮，縱切成兩半，再切5公分長段。

2 **1**料入鍋煮開，再入烏參煮2分鐘，撈起漂涼瀝乾。

3 鍋熱入油2大匙燒熱，入蔥、薑爆香，再入茄子、**2**料及水1杯煮開，續入烏參煮開，改小火煮至茄子變軟（約5分鐘），再以**3**料勾芡，最後淋上麻油並撒上蒜葉即可。

功效：含有豐富的蛋白質及膠質，營養高且容易消化，能促進發育，並有降血壓和防止便秘等功效。

$2/3$ lb. (300 g) .... sea cucumber	$1/4$ C. .... shredded fresh garlic spears
$8 3/4$ oz. (250 g) eggplant	$1/2$ t. .... sesame oil
4 sections green onion	
4 slices .... ginger root	

1
| 5 sections green onion |
| 4 slices ginger root |
| 4 C. water |
| 1 T. cooking wine |

2
| 2 T. soy sauce |
| $1/2$ T. cooking wine |
| $1/2$ t. sugar |
| $1/8$ t. pepper |

3
| 1 t. water |
| $1/2$ t. cornstarch |

1 Remove offal from sea cucumber and wash, cut each in half lengthwise, then cut into slanting strips. Wash and pare eggplant, cut in half lengthwise and cut into 2" (5 cm) long strips.

2 Bring **1** to a boil, add sea cucumber to boil for 2 minutes. Remove and rinse under cold water to cool. Drain.

3 Heat a wok, add 2 T. oil and heat. Stir-fry green onion and ginger roots until fragrant. Add eggplant,**2**and 1 C. water. Bring to a boil and add sea cucumber, again bring to a boil. Simmer over low heat until tender (about 5 minutes). Thicken with **3**, sprinkle on sesame oil and fresh garlic spears. Serve.

Functions: Rich in protein and gelatin. High nutritional value and easy to digest. May promote physical growth and lower blood pressure.

干貝花生 · Scallops and Peanuts

新鮮干貝		
..... 8兩（３００公克）		
蒜茸花生 .... $^1/_2$杯		
酒 .... 1 大匙		

1 ┌ 蒜片 .... 2 大匙
　 └ 紅辣椒片 .... 1 大匙

2 ┌ 鹽 .... $^1/_4$小匙
　 └ 味精 .... $^1/_8$小匙

1 干貝洗淨瀝乾，加酒拌勻醃１０分鐘，瀝乾備用。

2 鍋熱入油３杯燒至八分熱（約１８０℃），入干貝炸至金黃色，撈起瀝油。

3 鍋內留油$^1/_2$大匙，入 **1** 料炒香，再入炸好之干貝、花生及 **2** 料拌勻即可。

功效：有補血、健脾胃之功效，對產後乳汁不足者，有很好的療效。

$^2/_3$ lb. (300 g) .... fresh scallops
$^1/_2$ C. ...garlic peanuts
1 T. ..... cooking wine

1 ┌ 2 T. sliced garlic cloves
　 └ 1 T. sliced red chili pepper

2 $^1/_4$ t. salt

1 Wash scallops and pat dry. Marinate with wine for 10 minutes and drain.

2 Heat a wok, add 3 C. oil and heat to 350ºF (180ºC). Deep-fry scallops until golden brown. Remove and drain off the oil.

3 Retain $^1/_2$ T. oil in the wok. Stir-fry **1** until fragrant. Add scallops, peanuts and season with salt. Mix well and serve.

Functions: May replenish blood and regulate digestive organs. May promote milk production for nursing mothers.

芝麻魚乾 · Sesame Fish

小魚乾4兩（150公克）
熟芝麻 2大匙
蒜末 1大匙

1
水 1杯
糖 4大匙
酒 2大匙
醬油、米醋 .. 各1大匙

$^1/_3$ lb. (150 g) ... dried small fish
2 T. roasted sesame seeds
1 T. minced garlic cloves

1
1 C. water
4 T. sugar
2 T. cooking wine
1 T.each:soy sauce, rice vinegar

1 小魚乾沖水再泡軟（約15分鐘），瀝乾備用。

2 鍋熱入油6大匙燒熱，入魚乾炒至金黃色，續入蒜末炒香，再入**1**料煮開，改小火煮至湯汁收乾，最後入熟芝麻拌勻即可。

功效：含有豐富的鈣質和維他命D，適合小孩、發育中的青少年、孕婦及老人食用。

1 Soak dried fish until slightly soft (about 15 minutes). Drain.

2 Heat a wok, add 6 T. oil and heat. Fry the fish until golden brown. Add minced garlic cloves to fry until fragrant. Pour in **1** and bring to a boil. Turn the heat to low and simmer until all the sauce evaporates. Mix in sesame seeds and serve.

Functions: Rich in calcium and vitamin D. Good for children, teenagers, pregnant women and elderly people.

25

蜇皮拌蘿蔔絲 · Jellyfish Salad

海蜇皮6兩（２２５公克）
蔥............................ 1 枝
鹽........................ 1 小匙

2
┌ 麻油 ２大匙
│ 米醋 .... 1 ¹/₂ 大匙
│ 糖、醬油 各１大匙
└ 薑末 .... 2 小匙

1
┌ 白蘿蔔絲１５０公克
└ 胡蘿蔔絲１２０公克

¹/₂ lb. (225 g) jellyfish
1 stalk ... green onion
1 t. .... salt

1
┌ ¹/₃ lb. (150 g) shred-
│ ded turnip
│ 4 ¹/₄ oz. (120 g)
└ shredded carrot

2
┌ 2 T. sesame oil
│ 1 ¹/₂ T. rice vinegar
│ 1 T. each: sugar,
│ soy sauce
│ 2 t. minced ginger
└ roots

1 海蜇皮洗淨切絲，泡水２小時至軟，撈起瀝乾，以７０℃溫開水１０杯沖入，見海蜇皮稍捲曲，即入冷開水中漂涼，撈起瀝乾備用；蔥洗淨切絲泡水，待蔥絲捲起，隨即撈起備用。

2 **1**料入鹽拌醃至出水（約２０分鐘），續以冷開水漂洗三次，再稍擠乾水份，最後與海蜇皮及**2**料拌勻盛盤，並撒上蔥絲即可。

功效：含有豐富的維他命Ａ和Ｃ，適合高血壓、習慣性便秘者食用。

1 Wash jellyfish and shred; soak in water for 2 hours or until tender, drain. Pour warm water 150°F (70°C) into shredded jellyfish and soak until jellyfish shreds curl up slightly. Rinse immediately under cold water to cool. Drain. Wash green onion and shred; soak in cold water until green onion shreds curl up. Drain.

2 Mix **1** with salt and leave to stand (about 20 minutes). Drain off the liquid and rinse 3 times. Squeeze off excess water. Mix well with jellyfish and **2**. Sprinkle on shredded green onion and serve.

Functions: Rich in vitamin A and C. Good recipe for those with high blood pressure and constipation.

南瓜雞盅 · Chicken Pumpkin Cup

南瓜 ...2斤（1200公克）　蒜片 .... 2 大匙
雞胸肉 6兩（225公克）

1 ⎡ 醬油、太白粉 各2小匙
　 ⎢ 酒 .... 1 小匙
　 ⎣ 麻油 .... ¹/₂ 小匙

2 ⎡ 高湯 .... ³/₄ 杯
　 ⎢ 糖 .... 2 ¹/₂ 小匙
　 ⎢ 鹽 .... ³/₄ 小匙
　 ⎣ 味精 .... ¹/₄ 小匙

1　南瓜外皮刷洗乾淨，於蒂下¹/₃處橫切開，剩餘²/₃即為南瓜盅，將南瓜盅之瓜囊及籽去除，並用湯匙將部份瓜肉取下，使盅身約為1.5公分厚。

2　將取下之¹/₃南瓜去皮，挖去瓜囊，與取下之瓜肉均切小丁；雞胸肉洗淨，瀝乾切丁，入**1**料拌醃10分鐘，續入油1大匙拌勻。

3　鍋熱入油2大匙燒熱，入雞丁炒至變色取出；另鍋熱入油2大匙燒熱，入蒜片爆香，續入南瓜丁及**2**料拌煮至濃稠，再入雞丁拌勻即為內餡。

4　將內餡盛入南瓜盅內，盅口蓋上耐熱保鮮膜，入蒸鍋蒸至盅身熟透即可。

　功效：有健胃整腸、增強體力及延緩老化之功效，亦適合氣喘、糖尿病患者食用。

2 ²/₃ l b. (1200 g) .... pumpkin
¹/₂ lb. (225 g) chicken breast
2 T. sliced garlic cloves

1 ⎡ 2 t. each: soy sauce, cornstarch
　 ⎢ 1 t. cooking wine
　 ⎣ ¹/₂ t. sesame oil

2 ⎡ ³/₄ C. stock
　 ⎢ 2 ¹/₂ t. sugar
　 ⎣ ³/₄ t. salt

1　Brush and wash the pumpkin skin; cut the top off ¹/₃ below the stem widthwise. The remaining ²/₃ shall form a large pumpkin cup. Scoop the seeds and some pulp out, so the wall measures about ⁵/₈ " (1.5 cm) thick.

2　Remove the pulp off the top ¹/₃ and combine with the other pulp; then dice. Wash chicken breast and pat dry; dice. Marinate diced chicken breast in **1** for 10 minutes, then mix in 1 T. oil.

3　Heat a wok, add 2 T. oil and heat. Stir-fry diced chicken breast until the color changes, remove immediately. Heat another wok, add 2 T. oil and heat. Stir-fry sliced garlic cloves until fragrant. Add diced pumpkin pulp and **2**, cook until tender and the sauce is thick. Mix in chicken to complete the filling.

4　Fill the pumpkin cup with the filling, cover with a cellophane wrap and steam until tender, serve.

　Functions: May promote strength and delay aging process. Suitable also for asthma patients and diabetics.

薑芽豆豉雞 · Ginger Chicken in Black Bean Sauce

雞肉（帶骨）..................
.......１２兩（４５０公克）
青椒（１/₂個）....７５公克
嫩薑 ５６公克
蔥 １０段
紅辣椒 １條
豆豉 １大匙

1 ⎰ 酒、醬油 各１大匙
　　⎱ 太白粉 １小匙

2 ⎡ 水 .... ³/₄ 杯
　　⎢ 醬油 １大匙
　　⎣ 糖 .... ¹/₄ 小匙

1 雞肉洗淨，剁２×２公分塊狀，入**1**料拌醃２０分鐘；
　青椒及紅辣椒均洗淨，去籽切片；嫩薑洗淨切厚片；豆
　豉稍泡水，瀝乾備用。

2 鍋熱入油２大匙燒熱，入雞塊炒至變色，撈起備用。

3 鍋熱入油２大匙燒熱，入薑片煸炒數下，續入豆豉及蔥
　段炒香，再入雞塊及**2**料煮開，改小火蓋上鍋蓋煮至湯
　汁快收乾，最後再入青椒及辣椒炒勻即可。

功效：能袪風散寒，刺激食慾，補充元氣，適於冬季或
受風寒時食用。

1 lb. (450 g)...chicken
with bones
2 ¹/₂ oz. (75 g) .... green
bell pepper
2 oz. (56 g) .... baby
ginger roots
10 sections green onion
1 ...... red chili pepper

1 T. .... fermented
black beans

1 ⎡ 1 T. each: cooking
　　⎢ wine, soy sauce
　　⎣ 1 t. cornstarch

2 ⎡ ³/₄ C. water
　　⎢ 1 T. soy sauce
　　⎣ ¹/₄ t. sugar

1 Wash the chicken, chop into ³/₄" x ³/₄" (2 x 2 cm)
   square pieces, and marinate with **1** for 20 minutes.
   Wash green bell pepper and red chili pepper,
   discard the seeds and cut both into slices.
   Wash baby ginger roots and cut into thick
   slices. Soak fermented black beans in warm
   water until soft, drain.

2 Heat a wok, add 2 T. oil and heat. Stir-fry the
   chicken pieces until color changes. Remove.

3 Heat another wok, add 2 T. oil and heat. Stir-fry
   the ginger slices slightly. Add fermented black
   beans and green onion sections, stir-fry until
   fragrant. Then add chicken pieces and **2**, bring
   to a boil. Turn the heat to low and cover with a
   lid; simmer until the sauce nearly evaporates.
   Stir in green bell pepper and red chili pepper,
   mix well. Serve.

Functions: Improves appetite and can preclude
chills. Replenishes Chi. Good for winter or
when having a cold.

苦瓜燜雞翅 · Bitter Chicken Wings

雞翅12兩（450公克）
苦瓜（淨重）..................
...... 9兩（340公克）

2 ┌ 乾豆豉 1大匙
　　 └ 蒜末、辣椒末.............
　　 　 .... 各1小匙

1 ┌ 醬油 .... 1 $^1/_3$ 大匙
　　 │ 薑泥、黃酒、糖 ....
　　 └ 各1小匙

3 ┌ 水 1杯
　　 │ 糖 2小匙
　　 └ 鹽 .... $^1/_4$ 小匙

1 lb. (450 g) .. chicken wings

$^3/_4$ lb. (340 g) ... bitter melon

2 ┌ 1 T. dried fermented black beans
　　 │ 1 t. each: minced garlic cloves, minced
　　 └ red chili pepper

1 ┌ 1 $^1/_3$ T. soy sauce
　　 │ 1 t. each: ginger paste, Shao Hsing
　　 └ rice wine, sugar

3 ┌ 1 C. water
　　 │ 2 t. sugar
　　 └ $^1/_4$ t. salt

1 雞翅洗淨剁2公分長塊，入**1**料拌醃20分鐘；苦瓜洗淨，切2×3.5公分長塊，入開水中煮10分鐘，撈起漂涼瀝乾；豆豉稍泡軟，瀝乾備用。

2 鍋熱入油2大匙燒熱，入雞翅炒至變色取出，另鍋熱入油2大匙燒熱，入**2**料爆香，續入苦瓜、雞翅及**3**料煮開，改小火燜煮至湯汁快收乾（約20分鐘）即可。

功效：含豐富的維他命B、C及蛋白質，有消暑降火及清心明目之功效。

1 Wash chicken wings and chop into $^3/_4$" (2 cm) pieces, marinate in **1** for 20 minutes. Wash bitter melon, cut into $^3/_4$" x 1 $^3/_8$" (2 x 3.5 cm) pieces; cook in boiling water for 10 minutes, remove and rinse under cold water, drain. Soak fermented black beans in water until soft, drain.

2 Heat a wok, add 2 T. oil and heat. Stir-fry chicken wings until lightly golden, remove. Heat another wok, add 2 T. oil and heat. Stir-fry **2** until fragrant. Add bitter melon, chicken wings, and **3**; bring to a boil. Turn the heat to low and simmer until the sauce is nearly evaporated (about 20 minutes). Serve.

Functions: Rich in vitamin B, C, and protein. May reduce inner heat and brightens up the eyes. A good summer dish.

白果雞丁 · Gingko Chicken

雞胸肉6兩（２２５公克）
白果罐頭（去汁）..........
...... 4兩（１５０公克）
蔥...........................6段
薑...........................4片

1
水 .... 1 大匙
太白粉 .... $^1/_2$ 大匙
酒 .... 1 小匙
鹽 .... $^3/_8$ 小匙
味精 .... $^1/_8$ 小匙

2
水 .... 1 大匙
麻油 .... $^1/_2$ 小匙
鹽、味精... 各$^1/_4$小匙

$^1/_2$ lb.(225 g)...chicken breast
$^1/_3$ lb. (150 g)...canned gingko nuts (drained)
6 sections green onion
4 slices .... ginger root

1
1 T. water
$^1/_2$ T. cornstarch
1 t. cooking wine
$^3/_8$ t. salt

2
1 T. water
$^1/_2$ t. sesame oil
$^1/_4$ t. salt

1 雞胸肉洗淨，以刀背於表面交叉拍打後切小丁，入**1**料拌醃１０分鐘後，再入油１大匙拌勻；白果入開水中川燙，隨即撈起，瀝乾備用。

2 鍋熱入油２大匙燒熱，入蔥、薑爆香，續入雞丁炒至變色，再入白果拌勻，最後以**2**料調味即可。

功效：具止咳化痰、治濁止帶之功效，適合痰多喘咳、頻尿者、女性白帶過多或有白濁之現象者食用。

1 Wash chicken breast, pound the meat with the back of a knife; and cut into small cubes. Marinate in **1** for 10 minutes, then add 1 T. oil and mix well. Scald the gingko nuts in boiling water, remove and drain.

2 Heat a wok, add 2 T. oil and heat. Stir-fry green onion and ginger roots until fragrant. Add diced chicken to fry until color changes. Mix in gingko nuts. Season with **2** and serve.

Functions: May reduce coughing and liquefy sputum. A good dish for improving urine frequency and female vaginal discharges.

百合炒雞丁 · Lily Bulbs and Chicken

雞胸肉 6 兩（２２５公克）

新鮮百合 ....

...... 4 兩（１５０公克）

1
- 蛋白 .... $^1/_2$ 個
- 醬油 .... 1 大匙
- 太白粉 .... 2 小匙
- 胡椒粉 .... $^1/_8$ 小匙

2
- 水 .... $^1/_4$ 杯
- 番茄醬 .... 2 大匙
- 糖 .... $^1/_2$ 大匙
- 酒、麻油、米醋、太白
- 粉 .... 各 $^1/_2$ 小匙
- 鹽 .... $^1/_4$ 小匙
- 味精 .... $^1/_8$ 小匙

1 雞胸肉洗淨瀝乾，以刀背於表面交叉拍打後，切１．５ ×１．５公分寬小丁，續入**1**料拌醃１０分鐘，再入油 １大匙拌勻；新鮮百合一瓣瓣剝開洗淨，瀝乾備用。

2 鍋熱入油２大匙燒熱，入雞丁炒至變色，續入**2**料煮 開，再入百合拌炒數下即可。

功效：有潤肺止咳、清心安神之功效，小孩氣管弱者可 多食用。

$^1/_2$ lb. (225 g)...chicken breast

$^1/_3$ lb. (150 g)...fresh lily bulbs

1
- $^1/_2$ egg white
- 1 T. soy sauce
- 2 t. cornstarch
- $^1/_8$ t. pepper

2
- $^1/_4$ C. water
- 2 T. ketchup
- $^1/_2$ T. sugar
- $^1/_2$ t. each: cooking wine, sesame oil, rice vinegar, cornstarch
- $^1/_4$ t. salt

1 Wash chicken breast and pat dry. Pound the meat with the back of a knife and cut into $^5/_8$ " x $^5/_8$ " (1.5 x 1.5 cm) small cubes. Marinate in **1** for 10 minutes and then mix in 1 T. oil. Peel open lily bulbs and wash each petal and drain.

2 Heat a wok, add 2 T. oil and heat. Stir-fry chicken until color changes. Add **2** and bring to a boil. Add lily bulb petals, mix and stir slightly. Serve.

Functions: May relieve coughs and reduce anxiety. Ideal for children prone to bronchitis.

蘋果炒雞丁 · Apple Chicken

蘋果..8兩（３００公克）
雞胸肉...4兩（１５０公克）
四季豆 ８５公克
熟胡蘿蔔丁 ５６公克
蒜末 .... $^1/_2$ 大匙

1
太白粉、酒、水 ....
.... 各１小匙
鹽 .... $^1/_4$ 小匙
胡椒粉 .... $^1/_8$ 小匙

2
水 １大匙
太白粉、鹽 各 $^3/_8$ 小匙
味精 .... $^1/_8$ 小匙

$^2/_3$ lb. (300 g) .... apple
$^1/_3$ lb. (150 g)...chicken breast
3 oz. (85 g)....string beans
2 oz. (56 g) .... boiled and diced carrots
$^1/_2$ T. minced garlic cloves

1
1 t. each: water, cornstarch, cooking wine
$^1/_4$ t. salt
$^1/_8$ t. pepper

2
1 T. water
$^3/_8$ t. each: salt, cornstarch

1 蘋果洗淨去皮切丁，以鹽水（水４杯加鹽１小匙）浸泡約１０分鐘，撈起瀝乾水份；雞胸肉洗淨切丁，以**1**料拌醃１０分鐘後，入油１大匙拌勻；四季豆去老纖維洗淨，切１公分段備用。

2 鍋熱入油 $1\,^1/_2$ 大匙燒熱，入雞丁炒熟盛起。

3 另鍋入油２大匙燒熱，入蒜末爆香，續入四季豆及胡蘿蔔丁炒熟，再依序入蘋果、雞丁炒勻，最後入**2**料拌勻即可。

功效：具有補血、明目、促進食慾、幫助消化等功效。

1 Wash the apple, pare off the skin and dice. Marinate in brine (4 C. water and 1 t. salt) for 10 minutes; drain. Rinse chicken breast and dice; marinate in **1** for 10 minutes and mix in 1 T. oil. Remove the tough fibers on string beans and wash; cut into $^1/_2$" (1 cm) small sections.

2 Heat a wok, add $1\,^1/_2$ T. oil and heat. Stir-fry diced chicken until cooked.

3 Heat another wok, add 2 T. oil and heat. Stir-fry minced garlic cloves until fragrant. Stir in string beans and carrots, fry until tender. Mix in apple and chicken, season with **2**, serve.

Functions: May replenish blood, brighten up the eyes and may improve appetite and digestion.

檸檬雞片 · Lemon Chicken

雞胸肉..8兩（３００公克）
檸檬（1顆）.... ９０公克

2 ⎡ 太白粉 .... 4 大匙
⎣ 麵粉 .... 2 大匙

1 ⎡ 蛋黃 .... 1 個
  ⎜ 太白粉 .... 1 大匙
  ⎜ 醬油、酒... 各 ¹/₂ 大匙
  ⎜ 鹽 .... ¹/₄ 小匙
  ⎣ 胡椒粉 .... ¹/₈ 小匙

3 ⎡ 水 .... ¹/₂ 杯
  ⎜ 糖 .... 3 大匙
  ⎜ 太白粉 .... ¹/₂ 小匙
  ⎣ 鹽 .... ¹/₈ 小匙

²/₃ lb. (300 g)...chicken breast
3 ¹/₄ oz. (90 g) 1 lemon

2 ⎡ 4 T. cornstarch
⎣ 2 T. flour

1 ⎡ 1 egg yolk
  ⎜ 1 T. cornstarch
  ⎜ ¹/₂ T. each: soy
  ⎜ sauce, cooking wine
  ⎜ ¹/₄ t. salt
  ⎣ ¹/₈ t. pepper

3 ⎡ ¹/₂ C. water
  ⎜ 3 T. sugar
  ⎜ ¹/₂ t. cornstarch
  ⎣ ¹/₈ t. salt

1 雞胸肉洗淨瀝乾切大薄片，入 **1** 料拌醃，炸前再取出，一片片沾上拌勻之 **2** 料；檸檬洗淨切半，擠出部份汁液留用，再切成半圓形薄片狀。

2 鍋熱入油2杯燒至七分熱（１６０℃），將 ¹/₂ 份雞片一片片攤開入鍋，炸至淡金黃色，撈起瀝油，剩餘的雞片以同法炸至淺金黃色撈起，瀝油備用。

3 **3** 料及檸檬汁入鍋煮開，入雞片及檸檬片拌炒均勻。

功效：有消暑、生津、安胎、抗壞血病之作用，且有嫩膚美容功效。

1 Wash and pat dry chicken breast, then cut into large thin slices. Marinate in **1** . Dust with well-mixed **2** prior to frying. Wash lemon and cut in two, squeeze out some juice for later use, then cut the lemon into thin slices.

2 Heat a wok, add 2 C. oil and heat to 325°F (160°C). Spread out half of the chicken slices and deep-fry until lightly golden; remove and drain on kitchen towel. Fry remaining half the same way.

3 Bring **3** and lemon juice to a boil. Add deep-fried chicken slices and lemon. Mix evenly and serve.

Functions: A good summer dish to reduce inner heat and prevent thirst. May improve skin quality.

人參枸杞蒸雞 · Steamed Ginseng Chicken

去骨雞腿 .... 12兩（450公克）
人參鬚 10公克
枸杞子 1大匙

1⎰ 紹興酒 2小匙
  ⎱ 鹽 1小匙

2⎰ 水 1大匙
  ⎱ 太白粉 1小匙

1 lb. (450 g) boneless chicken legs
$^1/_3$ oz. (10 g) .... fibrous ginseng
1 T. .... lycium berries

1⎰ 2 t. Shao Hsing rice wine
  ⎱ 1 t. salt

2⎰ 1 T. water
  ⎱ 1 t. cornstarch

1 人參鬚剪碎，入熱開水$^1/_4$杯，加蓋燜5分鐘，待涼；枸杞子稍沖洗。

2 雞腿洗淨拭乾，置於深盤內，入**1**料、人參與汁液醃約20分鐘，加蓋入蒸鍋以大火蒸20分鐘後，取出，蒸汁留用。

3 將雞腿切片排盤，蒸汁及枸杞子入鍋煮開，並以**2**料勾芡，再淋於雞片上或當作沾料即可。

功效：具有補充體力，增強抵抗力之功效，亦可做為病後療養、恢復體力之食品。

1 Chop fibrous ginseng and soak in $^1/_4$ cup hot water; cover for 5 minutes and leave to cool. Rinse lycium berries.

2 Wash chicken legs and pat dry. Place the chicken in a deep dish, pour on **1**, ginseng and soaking water; marinate for 20 minutes. Cover the dish with a lid and steam in a steamer over high heat for 20 minutes. Remove the chicken legs. Retain the steam juice for later use.

3 Slice the chicken legs and arrange them on a plate. Bring steam juice and lycium berries to a boil and thicken with **2**. Pour the sauce over the chicken or serve the sauce on the side.

Functions: May promote strength and immunity. Ideal for recovering patients.

枸杞醉雞 · Drunken Chicken with Chinese Herb

全雞 1600公克
紹興酒 .... 1 ¹/₄ 杯

1
當歸 .... 1 片
鹽 .... 2 ¹/₃ 大匙
枸杞子 .... 2 大匙
味精 .... 1 小匙

3¹/₂ lb. (1600 g) chicken
1 ¹/₄ C. ..... Shao Hsing
rice wine

1
1 slice tangkuei
2 ¹/₃ T. salt
2 T. lycium berries

1 雞洗淨瀝乾，入開水中煮開（水量須蓋過雞身），再以大火煮10分鐘後熄火，續燜15分鐘後取出待涼，湯汁留用。

2 取約4杯雞湯，趁熱沖入**1**料內，待涼，續入紹興酒及雞浸泡過夜，再取出剁塊即可。

■ 泡雞時，醃汁須蓋過雞身，故須選擇較深及窄一點的容器，否則可將雞分切成3－4塊浸泡亦可。

功效：有保肝明目、強精補血之功效，對於假性近視、腰酸背痛及精蟲不足引起不孕者有療效。

1 Wash the chicken, pat dry and add into boiling water (water must cover the whole chicken). Boil over high heat for 10 minutes. Turn off the heat and let it stand covered for 15 more minutes. Remove the chicken and allow to cool. Retain the chicken broth for later use.

2 Pour 4 C. warm chicken broth into **1** and leave to cool. Add Shao Hsing rice wine. Marinate the chicken in wine broth overnight. Remove and cut into serving pieces.

■ The wine broth must cover the whole chicken. A deep and narrow container may be more suitable for marinating purposes. Or, the chicken may be cut into 3 or 4 large pieces before marinating.

Functions: May brighten up the eyes and reduce body aches.

百頁福袋 · Happy Purses

粉絲 ２０公克
百頁 １２張
干瓢（１５０公分長）.. １條
蔥絲 .... $^1/_4$杯
辣椒絲 １大匙

1┌ 絞肉 ....
  │ ４兩（１１５公克）
  └ 蝦仁、荸薺各５６公克

2┌ 水 ４杯
  └ 小蘇打 １小匙

3┌ 水、蔥末 各１大匙
  │ 麻油、酒、太白粉 ....
  │ 各１小匙
  │ 鹽 .... $^5/_8$小匙
  └ 胡椒粉 .... $^1/_4$小匙

4┌ 高湯 .... $^1/_2$杯
  │ 醬油 １大匙
  │ 麻油 ２小匙
  │ 太白粉 .... $^3/_4$小匙
  │ 糖 .... $^1/_2$小匙
  │ 鹽 .... $^1/_4$小匙
  └ 味精 .... $^1/_8$小匙

1 百頁入**2**料泡至變白色撈起，入冷水中漂洗至無滑潤感後撈起；干瓢泡軟，撈起瀝乾，切１２段；粉絲泡軟，切小段備用。

2 蝦仁去腸泥洗淨瀝乾，與絞肉分別剁碎，荸薺洗淨剁碎；將**1**料、**3**料及粉絲拌勻，並摔打數下，使之具有彈性，即為內餡，均分成１２等份備用。

3 取１張百頁包１份內餡，收口以干瓢綁住，即為百頁福袋，其餘依序做完置入深盤內，入蒸鍋以大火蒸１０分鐘取出，蒸汁留用。

4 **4**料及蒸汁入鍋煮開，續入蔥絲及辣椒絲再煮開，熄火，即為沾料。

功效：含有豐富的植物性、動物性蛋白質，具健脾益胃、壯陽補腎和消腫利濕之功效。

$^2/_3$ oz. (20 g) .... bean threads
12 .... bean curd sheets
5' (150 cm) .... dried gourd strips
$^1/_4$ C. ... shredded green onion
1 T. shredded red chili pepper

1┌ $^1/_4$ lb. (115 g) ground pork
  │ 2 oz. (56 g) each: shelled shrimp,
  └ water chestnuts

2┌ 4 C. water
  └ 1 t. baking soda

3┌ 1 T. each: water, minced green onion
  │ 1 t. each: sesame oil, cooking wine, cornstarch
  │ $^5/_8$ t. salt
  └ $^1/_4$ t. pepper

4┌ $^1/_2$ C. stock
  │ 1 T. soy sauce
  │ 2 t. sesame oil
  │ $^3/_4$ t. cornstarch
  │ $^1/_2$ t. sugar
  └ $^1/_4$ t. salt

1 Soak bean curd sheets in **2** until color pales, remove and rinse under cold water. Soak gourd strips in water until soft, drain and cut into 12 sections. Soak bean threads until soft, cut into short sections.

2 Devein the shrimp, wash and pat dry. Chop the shrimp and pork separately. Wash water chestnuts and chop fine. Mix **1**, **3**, and bean threads together, throw the mixture against a container to improve the texture. Divide the mixture into 12 equal filling portions.

3 Wrap each bean curd sheet with a portion of filling. Tighten the opening with a section of gourd shaving to resemble a purse. Arrange all the purses on a deep dish. Steam over high heat for 10 minutes. Remove and retain the juice.

4 Bring **4** and the juice to a boil. Add shredded green onion and shredded red chili pepper, bring to a boil again. This is the dipping sauce. Serve the purses with the sauce on the side.

Functions: Rich in both vegetable and animal protein. May improve internal organ functions.

冬瓜燒肉 · Don Quia Pork

冬瓜 .. 1斤（600公克）
五花肉9兩（340公克）

1▌
┌ 酒 .... ¹/₂ 杯
│ 醬油 .... 4 大匙
│ 冰糖 .... 1 大匙
│ 蔥 .... 2 枝
└ 薑 .... 6 片

1¹/₃ lb. (600 g) ..... d o n quia (pale squash)
³/₄ lb. (340 g) pork belly

1▌
┌ ¹/₂ C. cooking wine
│ 4 T. soy sauce
│ 1 T. rock sugar
│ 2 stalks green onion
└ 6 slices ginger root

1 五花肉洗淨切2×2×5公分塊狀，入開水中川燙，撈起漂涼瀝乾；冬瓜洗淨去皮及瓜囊，亦切同樣之大小；蔥洗淨切6公分長段備用。

2 鍋熱入油2大匙燒熱，入五花肉炒至表面微黃，續入 1▌ 料煮至濃稠，再入水6杯燜煮約1小時，最後入冬瓜煮至冬瓜熟軟（約30分鐘）即可。

功效：有補中益氣，利水消腫及清熱解毒之功效。

1 Wash pork and cut into ³/₄" x ³/₄" x 2" (2 x 2 x 5 cm) pieces, scald in boiling water. Remove and rinse under cold water, drain. Wash don quia, remove the skin and seeds, cut into the same size pieces as the pork. Wash the green onions and cut into 2 ¹/₂" (6 cm) sections.

2 Heat a wok, add 2 T. oil and heat. Stir-fry pork until slightly golden brown. Add 1▌ and cook until the sauce thickens. Add 6 C. water and simmer for one hour. Add don quia and cook until tender (about 30 minutes). Serve.

Functions: May promote chi. May improve edema and may have anti-toxic effect.

蓮藕肉片 · Lotus Roots and Pork

蓮藕 .. 8兩（３００公克）
里肌肉 １００公克
白醋 ２小匙

1⌈ 紅辣椒片 １大匙
 ⌊ 薑 ３片

2⌈ 醬油、酒、麻油 ....
 | 各１小匙
 | 太白粉 .... $^1/_2$小匙
 ⌊ 鹽 .... $^1/_8$小匙

3⌈ 糖、白醋各 2 $^1/_2$ 小匙
 ⌊ 鹽 .... $^1/_2$小匙

$^2/_3$ lb. (300 g) lotus roots
3 $^1/_2$ oz. (100 g) pork loin
2 t. .... white vinegar

1⌈ 1 T. sliced red chili
 | pepper
 ⌊ 3 slices ginger root

2⌈ 1 t. each: soy sauce,
 | cooking wine, sesame
 | oil
 | $^1/_2$ t. cornstarch
 ⌊ $^1/_8$ t. salt

3⌈ 2 $^1/_2$ t. each: sugar,
 | white vinegar
 ⌊ $^1/_2$ t. salt

1 蓮藕洗淨去皮，切薄片再切半，入醋水（水２杯入白醋２小匙）中浸泡，以防變色，使用前再漂水瀝乾；里肌肉洗淨切薄片入**2**料醃約１０分鐘。

2 鍋熱入油１杯燒至五分熱（１２０℃），入肉片炒至變色，撈起瀝油備用。

3 鍋內留油１$^1/_2$大匙燒熱，入**1**料爆香，再入蓮藕片及**3**料快炒數下，續入肉片拌勻即可。

功效：有開胃健脾、消暑氣、止瀉及補血等功效。

1 Wash and pare lotus roots, cut into thin slices, then into halves again. Soak in vinegar water (2 t. vinegar plus 2 C. water) to prevent discoloring. Drain prior to cooking. Wash pork loin and cut into thin slices, marinate in **2** for 10 minutes.

2 Heat a wok, add 1 C. oil and heat to 250°F (120°C). Stir-fry pork slices until color changes. Remove and drain off the oil.

3 Retain 1 $^1/_2$ T. oil in the wok, and heat. Stir-fry **1** until fragrant. Add lotus roots and **3**, stir-fry quickly. Mix in pork slices well and serve.

Functions: A good summer dish for reducing heat. May eliminate diarrhea and regulate digestive organs.

蔥爆里肌 · Stir-fried Pork with Green Onions

里肌肉 .. 8兩（３００公克）
蔥 4 兩 ....（１５０公克）

1
┌ 醬油、水 各１大匙
│ 蒜末、酒、太白粉 ....
│ .... 各 $^1/_2$ 大匙
└ 糖 .... 1 小匙

2
┌ 水 .... 1 大匙
│ 醬油 .... 2 小匙
│ 糖 .... $^1/_2$ 小匙
│ 味精、花椒粉 ....
└ .... 各 $^1/_8$ 小匙

$^2/_3$ lb. (300 g) pork loin
$^1/_3$ lb. (150 g) green onions

1
┌ 1 T. each: soy sauce,
│ water
│ $^1/_2$ T. each: minced
│ garlic cloves, cooking
│ wine, cornstarch
└ 1 t. sugar

2
┌ 1 T. water
│ 2 t. soy sauce
│ $^1/_2$ t. sugar
│ $^1/_8$ t. Szechwan
└ peppercorn powder

1 里肌肉洗淨切 1.5×5 公分薄片，入**1**料拌醃 1０分鐘後，續入油１大匙拌勻；蔥洗淨切 3 公分段，再將蔥白及蔥綠分開備用。

2 鍋熱入油 2 大匙燒熱，入里肌肉炒至變色盛起；另鍋熱入油 1 大匙燒熱，入蔥白炒香，再入肉、蔥綠及**2**料拌炒均勻即可。

　功效：具發汗、殺菌、祛痰及開胃、利尿之作用；受風寒而導致發燒、無汗及胃口不佳者皆宜食用。

1 Wash pork loin and cut thin slices ($^5/_8$" x 2" or 1.5 x 5 cm). Marinate the pork slices in **1** for 10 minutes, then mix in 1 T. oil. Wash green onions and cut into $1\,^1/_4$" (3 cm) sections; separate the green and white parts.

2 Heat a wok, add 2 T. oil and heat. Stir-fry pork until color changes; remove. Heat another wok, add 1 T. oil and heat. Stir-fry white parts of green onion until fragrant. Add pork, green onion parts and **2**; mix well. Serve.

Functions: May improve cold condition and liquefy sputum. May increase urine frequency.

鹹蛋蒸肉餅 · Steamed Meat Patty with Salted Eggs

絞肉 .. 6兩（２２５公克）
豆腐（¹/₂塊）................
.... 3兩（１１５公克）
生鹹蛋 2個

1
醬油 .... 1 大匙
酒、麻油 .. 各¹/₂大匙
蔥末 .... 1 小匙
糖、太白粉、胡椒粉 ..
.... 各¹/₄小匙
味精 .... ¹/₈小匙

¹/₂ lb. (225 g) ground pork
¹/₄ lb. (115 g) ...... tofu
2 .... raw salty eggs

1
1 T. soy sauce
¹/₂ T. each: cooking
wine, sesame oil
1 t. minced green
onion
¹/₄ t. each:sugar,
cornstarch, pepper

1 絞肉再剁細；豆腐去硬邊壓成泥；生鹹蛋去殼、蛋黃切半，用刀背稍壓扁，鹹蛋白留一個備用。

2 絞肉、豆腐、鹹蛋白及 **1** 料拌勻，並摔打數下，使之具有彈性。

3 取一圓形容器，入作法 2 之材料，表面抹平，上舖蛋黃，封上保鮮膜，入鍋以大火蒸熟（約１５分鐘）。

功效：含有豐富的蛋白質、脂肪、鈣、磷及維生素，兒童食用可促進食慾並助其生長，增加智慧。

1 Chop ground pork with a knife. Trim off the firm edges from the tofu block and crush to a paste. Remove the salty egg shell and cut the yolks to halves; flatten the yolks with the back of a knife. Keep one egg white for later use.

2 Mix pork, tofu, salty egg white and **1** well; throw the mixture against the mixing bowl a few times to improve the texture.

3 Place the meat patty mixture into a round container; even the surface with a spatula. Place the egg yolks on top. Cover with cellophane paper and steam over high heat until done (about 15 minutes). Serve.

Functions: It is rich with protein, fat, calcium, minerals and vitamins. Good nutrition for children.

牛肉腐皮捲 · Beef Tofu Rolls

牛絞肉、洋蔥 各135公克
豆腐皮 3張

1
蔥末、醬油、水 各1大匙
糖、酒、太白粉 各1小匙
薑泥、麻油 各 $^3/_4$ 小匙

2 麵粉、水 各1大匙

4 $^3/_4$ oz. (135 g) each:
ground beef, onion
3 bean curd sheets

1
1 T. each: minced
green onion, soy
sauce, water
1 t. each: cooking
wine, cornstarch,
sugar
$^3/_4$ t. each: ginger
paste, sesame oil

2 1 T. each: flour, water

1 洋蔥洗淨切細丁；鍋熱入油 1 $^1/_2$ 大匙燒熱，入洋蔥炒
軟，盛起；豆腐皮每張剪成4小張，共12張；**2**料調
匀成麵糊備用。

2 牛絞肉再剁細，入 **1** 料拌匀，並摔打數下，使之具有
彈性，續入洋蔥拌匀即為內餡，分成12等份。

3 取1張豆腐皮，中間放1份內餡，捲起包成春捲狀，接
口處以**2**料黏緊，即為腐皮捲。

4 平底鍋燒熱入油2大匙燒熱，入腐皮捲以小火煎至兩面
呈金黃色即可。食時可沾番茄醬。

功效：含有豐富的蛋白質及鐵質，能補充體力、消除疲
勞，是病後及產後的滋養食品。

1 Wash the onion and dice. Heat a wok, add 1 $^1/_2$ T.
oil and heat. Stir-fry diced onion until tender,
remove. Snip each bean curd sheet to 4 small
sheets, totaling 12 sheets. Mix **2** evenly into a
paste.

2 Chop ground beef with a knife. Mix well with
1 and throw the meat mixture against the container a few times to improve the texture. Then
mix in fried onion evenly. Divide the mixture
into 12 equal portions.

3 Wrap each bean curd sheet around a portion of
meat filling and shape into a spring roll. Seal
the openings with well-mixed **2** .

4 Heat a skillet, add 2 T. oil and heat. Fry the rolls
over low heat until golden brown on both sides.
May be served with ketchup.

Functions: Rich in protein and iron. May reduce
fatigue. Ideal for recovering patients or postnatal
women.

紅燴牛腩 · Tomato Beef Stew

牛腩１２兩（４５０公克）
番茄 .. ８兩（３００公克）
洋蔥 .. ６兩（２２５公克）

2
┌ 番茄醬 ３大匙
│ 醬油、酒 各２大匙
└ 冰糖 １小匙

1
┌ 蔥 ６段
└ 薑 ４片

1 lb. (450 g) beef brisket
²/₃ lb. (300 g) tomatoes
¹/₂ lb. (225 g) ....onions

1
┌ 6 sections green
│ onion
└ 4 slices ginger root

2
┌ 3 T. ketchup
│ 2 T. each: soy sauce,
│ cooking wine
└ 1 t. rock sugar

1 牛腩洗淨切４公分長塊，入開水中川燙，撈起漂涼，瀝乾；番茄洗淨，底部劃十字，入開水中煮至皮掀起，撈起漂涼，去皮及籽後切塊；洋蔥洗淨亦切塊。

2 鍋熱入油２大匙燒熱，入洋蔥炒香，續入番茄炒軟，盛起備用。

3 鍋續入油１大匙燒熱，入**1**料爆香，續入牛腩及**2**料炒勻，再入水４杯煮開，改小火加蓋燜煮至肉軟，再入洋蔥及番茄煮至湯汁濃稠即可。

■ 牛腩可以牛尾代替，其餘作法不變。

功效：能促進食慾，補益氣血，調節新陳代謝，預防皮膚粗糙等功效。

1 Wash beef brisket and cut into 1 ¹/₂ " (4 cm) pieces. Scald beef in boiling water, remove and rinse under cold water; drain. Wash tomatoes, score a cross at each bottom, scald in boiling water until skins curl up; remove and rinse under cold water. Pare off the skins, remove the seeds, and cut the tomatoes into pieces. Wash onions and cut into pieces.

2 Heat a wok, add 2 T. oil and heat. Stir-fry onions until fragrant. Add tomatoes and stir-fry until tender. Remove onto a plate.

3 Add 1 T. oil in the wok, stir-fry **1** until fragrant. Mix in the beef and **2**. Pour in 4 C. water and bring to a boil. Turn the heat to low and simmer covered until tender. Add onion and tomato mixture, simmer until the sauce thickens. Serve.

■ Beef brisket may be replaced by ox tails.

Functions: May improve appetite, replenish chi and blood. May improve metabolism and prevent coarse skin.

紅燒牛蒡肉 · Gobo Beef Stew

牛腩１２兩（４５０公克）
牛蒡（淨重）..................
.... ４兩（１５０公克）
麻油 １小匙

1┌ 蔥 ５段
 │ 薑 ３片
 │ 酒 １大匙
 └ 八角 ２顆

2┌ 醬油 １¹/₂大匙
 │ 紅辣椒片 １大匙
 └ 糖 １小匙

3┌ 水 ２小匙
 └ 太白粉 １小匙

1 牛腩洗淨切４公分長塊，入開水中川燙，撈起漂涼，洗淨瀝乾；牛蒡洗淨去皮，切滾刀塊備用。

2 鍋內入牛腩、**1**料及水１０杯，以大火煮開，改小火燜煮約１小時，去蔥、薑及八角，加入牛蒡，及**2**料續煮至牛蒡入味（約３０分鐘），再以**3**料勾芡，最後淋上麻油即可。

功效：有整腸、利尿、降血壓及抗癌之功效。

1 lb. (450 g) beef brisket
¹/₃ lb. (150 g) burdock
1 t. sesame oil

1┌ 5 sections green on-
 │ ion
 │ 3 slices ginger root
 │ 1 T. cooking wine
 └ 2 star anises

2┌ 1 ¹/₂ T. soy sauce
 │ 1 T. sliced red chili
 │ pepper
 └ 1 t. sugar

3┌ 2 t. water
 └ 1 t. cornstarch

1 Wash beef brisket and cut into 1 ¹/₂" (4 cm) pieces; scald in boiling water for a while. Remove and rinse under cold water to cool, drain. Wash and pare burdock, cut into diagonal pieces.

2 Bring beef, **1**, and 10 C. water to a boil over high heat. Turn the heat to low and simmer until tender (about 1 hour). Discard green onion, ginger roots and star anises. Add burdock pieces and **2**, cook until taste permeates burdock (about 30 minutes). Thicken with **3** and sprinkle on sesame oil. Serve.

Functions: May regulate intestinal movements, act as a diuretic, and lower blood pressure.

44

牛蒡炒牛肉 · Gobo Beef

牛里肌、牛蒡各150公克
薑絲、熟芝麻 ... 各1大匙

1
┌ 水 .... ¹/₂ 大匙
├ 醬油 .... 2 小匙
└ 太白粉 .... 1 小匙

2
┌ 水 .... ¹/₂ 杯
├ 酒 .... 2 大匙
├ 醬油 .... 1 ¹/₃ 大匙
├ 糖 .... 1 大匙
├ 米醋 .... 1 小匙
└ 味精 .... ¹/₈ 小匙

1 牛里肌洗淨切絲,入**1**料醃10分鐘,續入油1大匙拌匀;牛蒡去皮洗淨,斜切薄片再切細絲,泡水以防變色,待炒時再瀝乾。

2 鍋熱入油2大匙燒熱,入牛肉炒至變色,隨即撈起。

3 另鍋熱入油3大匙燒熱,入薑絲爆香,續入牛蒡拌炒數下,隨即入**2**料以中火煮至牛蒡軟化且汁收乾時,再入牛肉以大火炒匀,熄火起鍋,並撒上芝麻即可。

功效:具有促進血液循環,新陳代謝及整腸之功能。另牛蒡具有降低膽固醇、降血壓、抗癌、補腎、強身之功效。

¹/₃ lb. (150 g) each: beef
filet, burdock
1 T. each: shredded
ginger roots, roasted
sesame seeds

2
┌ ¹/₂ C. water
├ 2 T. cooking wine
├ 1 ¹/₃ T. soy sauce
├ 1 T. sugar
└ 1 t. rice vinegar

1
┌ ¹/₂ T. water
├ 2 t. soy sauce
└ 1 t. cornstarch

1 Wash beef filet then shred; marinate with **1** for 10 minutes; then mix in 1 T. oil. Wash and pare burdock then shred; soak in water to prevent discoloring. Drain off the water before cooking.

2 Heat a wok, add 2 T. oil and heat. Stir-fry the beef quickly until color pales, remove.

3 Heat another wok, add 3 T. oil and heat. Stir-fry ginger roots until fragrant. Stir-fry burdock slightly. Then add **2** and cook over medium heat until tender and the sauce is nearly evaporated. Add the beef and stir-fry over high heat. Remove and sprinkle on sesame seeds. Serve.

Functions: Can increase blood circulation and metabolism. Burdock is especially good for lowering cholesterol and blood pressure.

洋蔥炒羊肉 · Stir-fried Onion Lamb

洋蔥 .. 8兩（３００公克）
羊肉片（火鍋用）...........
.... 6兩（２２５公克）

1 ┌ 味全烤肉醬 1 ¹/₂ 大匙
  ├ 甜麵醬、酒 .. 各 2 小匙
  └ 醬油 .... 1 小匙

²/₃ lb. (300 g) .... onion
¹/₂ lb. (225 g) thin sliced lamb (for Shabu Shabu)

1 ┌ 1 ¹/₂ T. Wei Chuan B-B-Q sauce
  ├ 2 t. each: sweet bean paste, cooking wine
  └ 1 t. soy sauce

1 **1** 料拌勻；洋蔥洗淨去皮，切絲備用。

2 鍋熱入油 1 ¹/₂ 大匙燒熱，入洋蔥絲炒香，續入 **1** 料炒至入味（約3分鐘），再入羊肉片拌炒，至肉片變色。

功效：羊肉有補虛勞、益氣血之功效，貧血、低血壓、體質虛寒及四肢容易冰冷的人宜多食用。

1 Mix all ingredients in **1** well. Wash onions, remove the skin and shred.

2 Heat a wok, add 1 ¹/₂ T. oil and heat. Stir-fry shredded onions until fragrant. Add **1** and stir-fry until taste permeates the mixture (about 3 minutes). Add lamb slices and stir-fry until lamb color changes. Serve.

Functions: Lamb may reduce fatigue, and chills, while improving blood circulation. Suitable for those have low blood pressure, anaemia and cold limbs.

糖心蛋 · Gourmet Eggs

蛋............................ 6 個
鹽........................ 1 小匙

1
水.............. 2 $^1/_2$ 杯
醬油 .... $^1/_2$ 杯
冰糖 .... 8 大匙
八角 .... 1 顆

6 .... eggs
1 t. .... salt

1
2 $^1/_2$ C. water
$^1/_2$ C. soy sauce
8 T. rock sugar
1 star anise

1 **1** 料入鍋煮開,改小火加蓋續煮 5 分鐘,熄火待涼即為滷汁。

2 深鍋入水 3 杯及鹽煮開,入冷水 2 杯及蛋以中火煮開,續煮 3 分鐘,隨即撈起,入冰開水中泡涼。

3 將蛋殼輕壓,使之產生細碎之裂紋,輕輕撥去蛋殼,再入滷汁中浸泡過夜即可。

功效:蛋可增強體力,延遲老化。

1 Bring **1** to a boil, simmer over low heat for 5 minutes. Allow to cool. This is the marinating sauce.

2 Bring 3 C. water and salt to a boil. Add 2 C. cold water and the eggs; bring to boil over medium heat. Boil for 3 minutes. Remove the eggs and soak in ice water to cool.

3 Gently remove the shells and soak the eggs in marinating sauce overnight. Cut into halves and serve cold.

Functions: May increase energy.

蘑菇滑蛋 ▪ Simple Mushroom Omelet

新鮮洋菇（淨重）..............
.... 4兩（１５０公克）
蛋............................ 4個
蔥末 2大匙

1
水 .... 1 大匙
酒................. 1 小匙
鹽................. $^1/_4$ 小匙

2
鹽、粗黑胡椒粉 ....
.... 各$^1/_4$ 小匙
味精 .... $^1/_8$ 小匙

$^1/_3$ lb. (150 g) mushrooms
4 .... eggs
2 T. minced green onion

1
1 T. water
1 t. cooking wine
$^1/_4$ t. salt

2
$^1/_4$ t. each: salt, black pepper powder

1 洋菇洗淨切片，入開水中川燙撈起，漂涼瀝乾；蛋去殼打散，入 **1**料拌勻備用。

2 鍋熱入油３大匙燒熱，入蔥末爆香，續入洋菇片及**2**料炒勻，再入蛋液，以鍋鏟稍攪動，見蛋液稍凝固，即熄火起鍋。

功效：含有豐富的蛋白質、多醣體、維他命 B，能提高免疫能力，適合體質較虛弱及病後療養者食用。

1 Wash the mushrooms and slice. Scald in boiling water and rinse under cold water to cool; drain. Beat the eggs and mix well with **1**.

2 Heat a wok, add 3 T. oil and heat. Stir-fry minced green onion until fragrant. Add mushrooms and **2**, stir-fry and mix well. Pour in beaten eggs, stir gently with a spatula until slightly set. Remove immediately and serve.

Functions: Rich in protein, polysaccharide and vitamin B. May improve immunity. Ideal for recovering patients.

蔬菜小魚烘蛋 · Surprise Egg Cake

四季豆、銀魚...各５６公克　　酒.................... 2 小匙
蛋............................. 3 個　　太白粉 .... ¹/₄ 小匙
蒜末 .... 2 小匙

2 oz. (56 g) each: string beans, silver fish
3 .... eggs
2 t. minced garlic cloves

2 t. cooking wine
¹/₄ t. cornstarch

1　四季豆去老纖維後洗淨切碎；銀魚稍沖洗，瀝乾備用。

2　鍋熱入油１大匙燒熱，入蒜末炒香，連油盛起待涼即為蒜油，備用。

3　蛋去殼打散，入四季豆、銀魚、蒜油及１料拌勻。

4　鍋續入油２大匙燒熱，入蛋液加蓋，以小火烘至半凝固狀，翻面再烘２分鐘即可。

功效：含有豐富的蛋白質和鈣質，尤其適合生長期的孩子及懷孕中的婦女食用。

1　Trim the tough fiber off the string beans, wash then chop fine. Rinse the silver fish and drain.

2　Heat a wok, add 1 T. oil and heat. Stir-fry minced garlic cloves until fragrant. Remove both garlic and oil to a small bowl for later use.

3　Beat the eggs, add chopped string beans, silver fish, garlic oil, and **1** . Mix well.

4　Heat a wok, add 2 T. oil and heat. Pour in the egg mixture, cover with a lid and pot roast over low heat until half set. Turn the egg cake to the other side and pot roast 2 more minutes. Serve.

Functions: Rich in protein and calcium. Ideal for children and pregnant women.

水晶蛋絲 · Agar-agar Salad

小黃瓜4兩（１５０公克）
蟹肉棒 ７５公克
蛋 ３個
洋菜（４公分段）..... １杯
鹽 .... ¹/₂小匙

1
┌ 醬油 .... 1 ¹/₂ 大匙
│ 麻油、米醋 ... 各１大匙
│ 細砂糖 １小匙
└ 味精 .... ¹/₄小匙

¹/₃ lb.(150 g)... gherkin cucumbers
2 ¹/₂ oz. (75 g) imitated crab meat
3 .... eggs
1 C. agar-agar, 1 ¹/₂"
(4 cm) long sections

¹/₂ t. .... salt

1
┌ 1 ¹/₂ T. soy sauce
│ 1 T. each: sesame
│ oil, rice vinegar
└ 1 t. sugar

1 小黃瓜洗淨切絲，入鹽拌醃至出水（約２０分鐘），續以冷開水漂洗三次，再稍擠乾水份；蟹肉棒拆絲，入開水中稍川燙，隨即撈起瀝乾；洋菜入溫開水中泡軟取出，瀝乾拆絲；蛋去殼打散備用。

2 平底鍋燒熱，入油１小匙，用刷子在鍋內刷勻，入¹/₂蛋液以小火煎成蛋皮，取出待涼切絲，另１份依序完成。

3 將洋菜鋪於盤底，依序排上蛋絲、黃瓜絲及蟹肉絲，食時再淋上拌勻之**1**料即可。

功效：具清涼降火，促進食慾，補充體力，是夏季極佳之菜餚。

1 Wash and shred gherkin cucumbers, marinate with salt until water seeps out (about 20 minutes). Rinse with cold water and squeeze off the water and pat dry. Tear the crab meat to shreds, scald in boiling water; remove immediately and rinse to cool, drain. Soak agar-agar in lukewarm water until soft; drain and tear to shreds. Beat the eggs.

2 Heat a pan, brush on 1 t. oil. Pour in ¹/₂ beaten eggs to make egg crepes over low heat. Allow egg crepes to cool, then shred. Repeat the process until all are made.

3 Arrange agar-agar on a plate, then arrange, by the order of, eggs, cucumbers, and crab meat on top. Pour over well-mixed **1** sauce over and serve.

Functions: An ideal summer dish for cooling inner heat and rejuvenating strength.

韭菜煎蛋 · Chive Egg Cake

韭菜 .... 3 兩（115 克）
蛋 .... 4 個

1
┌ 蔥末 .... 1 大匙
│ 沙拉油 .... 2 小匙
│ 太白粉、鹽各 $^1/_2$ 小匙
└ 味精 .... $^1/_8$ 小匙

$^1/_4$ lb. (115 g) Chinese
chives
4 .... eggs

1
┌ 1 T. minced green
│ onion
│ 2 t. salad oil
│ $^1/_2$ t. each: salt,
└ cornstarch

1 韭菜洗淨切小丁；蛋去殼打散，入 1 料及韭菜拌勻。

2 鍋熱入油 3 大匙燒熱，潤鍋後，續入蛋液煎至兩面呈金
黃色即可。

功效：含有豐富的蛋白質和維他命 A、B、C，可增進
食慾、促進荷爾蒙分泌和血液循環及改善虛冷體質。

1 Wash the Chinese chives and chop. Beat the eggs,
add 1 and chopped chives.

2 Heat a wok, add 3 T. oil and heat. Oil the pan and
pour in the egg mixture and fry until golden on
both sides.

Functions: High in protein and vitamin A, B, and
C. May improve appetite and blood circulation.

51

油菜燒豆腐 · Braised You-choy Tofu

油菜.... 8兩（300公克）
油豆腐6兩（225公克）
蒜末 .... 1 小匙

1
┌ 高湯 .... 1 杯
│ 醬油、酒 ... 各 $^1/_2$ 大匙
│ 糖、鹽 ..... 各 $^1/_2$ 小匙
└ 味精 .... $^1/_8$ 小匙

2
┌ 水 .... $^1/_2$ 大匙
└ 太白粉 .... $^1/_2$ 小匙

$^2/_3$ lb. (300 g) you-choy (rape)

$^1/_2$ lb. (225 g) fried tofu

1 t. minced garlic cloves

1
┌ 1 C. stock
│ $^1/_2$ T. each: soy sauce, cooking wine
│ $^1/_2$ t. each: sugar, salt

2
┌ $^1/_2$ T. water
└ $^1/_2$ t. cornstarch

1 油菜洗淨切3公分長段，將葉及梗分開；油豆腐稍沖洗後各切成8小塊備用。

2 鍋熱入油2大匙燒熱，入蒜末爆香，續入油菜梗炒勻，再入**1**料及油豆腐煮開，改小火煮至湯汁剩約 $^1/_3$ 杯時，入油菜葉炒軟，並以**2**料勾芡即可。

功效：有生津潤燥、清熱解毒、散血消腫之作用。

1 Wash you-choy and cut into $1^1/_4$ " (3 cm) sections; divide the stems and leaves. Rinse tofu and cut into 8 small pieces.

2 Heat a wok, add 2 T. oil and heat. Stir-fry garlic cloves until fragrant. Add you-choy stems to fry. Then add **1** and tofu, bring it to a boil. Turn the heat to low and simmer until the sauce reduces to $^1/_3$ C. Mix in you-choy leaves and cook until tender. Thicken with **2**. Serve.

Functions: May relieve thirst and promote saliva. May reduce inner heat and correct edema.

雪菜燒豆腐 · Tofu Casserole

凍豆腐（２塊）..............
...... １２兩（４５０公克）

黃雪裡紅 ７５公克
絞肉 ３大匙
酒 １大匙

1
┌ 鹹魚丁 ２８公克
│ 紅辣椒片、蔥末 ....
│ 各１大匙
└ 薑末 １小匙

2
┌ 高湯 .... １ $1/_3$ 杯
│ 酒 １大匙
│ 醬油 .... $1/_2$ 大匙
│ 糖 .... $3/_4$ 小匙
└ 味精 .... $1/_8$ 小匙

1 凍豆腐切四方塊；黃雪裡紅洗淨切末。

2 鍋熱入油２大匙燒熱，入 **1** 料爆香，續入絞肉及酒炒熟，再入黃雪裡紅炒勻，盛起分成２等份。

3 取１砂鍋，鍋底先放１份炒好之肉末雪裡紅，續依序入豆腐及另１份肉末雪裡紅，再淋上 **2** 料煮開，改小火加蓋燜煮２０分鐘即可。

功效：有祛風散寒，開胃消食和化痰等功效。

1 lb. (450 g) ....2 blocks
frozen bean curds

2 $1/_2$ oz. (75 g)...yellow
salted mustard greens
3 T. .... ground pork
1 T. ...... cooking wine

1
┌ 1 oz. (28 g) diced
│ salted fish
│ 1 T. each: sliced red
│ chili pepper, minced
│ green onion
│ 1 t. minced ginger
└ roots

2
┌ 1 $1/_3$ C. stock
│ 1 T. cooking wine
│ $1/_2$ T. soy sauce
└ $3/_4$ t. sugar

1 Cut each block of frozen tofu into four pieces. Wash mustard greens and chop fine.

2 Heat a wok, add 2 T. oil and heat. Stir-fry **1** until fragrant. Add pork and cooking wine, stir-fry until cooked. Add mustard greens, mix well and remove. Divide into 2 equal portions.

3 Place a portion of the pork mixture at the bottom of a casserole, add a layer of tofu, then top with a layer of the pork mixture. Pour the **2** on top and bring to a boil. Simmer over low heat, covered with a lid, for 20 minutes. Serve.

Functions: May improve cold conditions.

黃豆燒海帶 · Braised Soy Beans with Seaweed

黃豆 .. 3兩（１１５公克）
乾海帶 ２０公克

1
水 .... 4 杯
醬油 .... ２ 大匙
米醋 .... １ 大匙

2 酒、糖 各１大匙

$^1/_4$ lb. (115 g) soy beans
$^2/_3$ oz. (20 g).....seaweed

1
4 C. water
2 T. soy sauce
1 T. rice vinegar

2
1 T. each: cooking wine, sugar

1 黃豆洗淨，泡溫水漲至２倍大（約４小時）瀝乾；海帶稍沖洗後泡軟，切小片備用。

2 鍋熱入油２大匙燒熱，入黃豆炒數下，再入**1**料煮開，改小火加蓋燜煮至黃豆軟化（約１$^1/_2$小時），續入海帶及**2**料，以大火炒至湯汁快收乾即可。

功效：能預防高血壓、腦血管病變及甲狀腺腫大，且具抗氧化作用，可防止老化。

1 Wash the soy beans and soak in warm water until they swell to double size (about 4 hours), drain. Rinse seaweed and soak until soft; dice.

2 Heat a wok, add 2 T. oil and heat. Stir-fry the soy beans slightly, add **1** and bring to a boil. Cover with a lid and simmer until tender (about one and half hours). Add seaweed and **2**. Stir-fry over high heat until the sauce is nearly evaporated. Serve.

Functions: Can prevent high blood pressure and swollen thyroid. Has anti-oxidizing and anti-aging effects.

雙冬麵輪 · Vegetarian Special

熟筍 ... 4兩（150公克）
麵輪 110公克
香菇 8朵

1
水 1¹/₂杯
醬油 2¹/₂大匙
酒 .... ¹/₂大匙
糖 1小匙

¹/₃ lb. (150 g) ... boiled bamboo shoots
4 oz. (110 g) ..... wheat gluten wheels
8 .... Chinese black mushrooms

1
1 ¹/₂ C. water
2 ¹/₂ T. soy sauce
¹/₂ T. cooking wine
1 t. sugar

1 麵輪入開水中煮5分鐘，撈起漂涼，擠乾水份；熟筍切厚片；香菇泡軟洗淨去蒂切半備用。

2 鍋熱入油2大匙燒熱，入香菇片爆香，續入筍片、麵輪及**1**料煮開，改小火加蓋，燜煮至湯汁收乾（每隔5分鐘翻面一次，以免焦底）即可。

功效：為高纖維、低熱量菜餚，具有整腸助消化之功效，是適合營養過剩之現代人的一道美食。

1 Boil the wheat gluten wheels in boiling water for 5 minutes; remove and squeeze out the water. Cut bamboo shoots into thick slices. Soak Chinese black mushrooms, in warm water until soft, rinse and discard the stems; then cut into halves.

2 Heat a wok, add 2 T. oil and heat. Stir-fry mushroom slices until fragrant. Add bamboo shoot slices, gulten wheat wheels and **1**; bring to a boil. Turn the heat to low and simmer covered until the sauce is completely evaporated (stir every 5 minutes to prevent sticking at the bottom). Serve.

Functions: An ideal dish of high fiber and low calories for the over-eating modern person. May improve digestive organs.

髮菜素雞 · Stir-fried Wheat Gluten Sausages

麵腸 .. 9兩（３４０公克）　麻油 .... 1 小匙
芹菜 ５６公克
香菇 8朵
蔥.............................. 6 段
髮菜 .... ¹/₂杯
辣椒絲 .... 1 大匙

1
高湯 .... ¹/₂杯
醬油 .... 1 大匙
糖、鹽 ..... 各¹/₂小匙
味精 .... ¹/₈小匙

³/₄ lb. (340 g)......wheat gluten sausages
2 oz. (56 g) .... celery
8...............Chinese black mushrooms
6 sections green onion
¹/₂ C. dried black moss
1 T. shredded red chili pepper

1 t. .... sesame oil

1
¹/₂ C. stock
1 T. soy sauce
¹/₂ t. each: sugar, salt

1 麵腸洗淨直切成兩半，再切小片；髮菜洗淨泡軟瀝乾；香菇洗淨泡軟去蒂切粗絲；芹菜去根及葉洗淨，切３公分長段再稍拍扁。

2 鍋熱入油３大匙燒熱，入蔥段及香菇爆香，續入麵腸煸炒至微焦黃，再入髮菜及**1**料炒至湯汁收乾，最後入芹菜、辣椒及麻油拌炒均勻即可。

功效：含豐富的蛋白質和鐵質，具有補血作用，常吃可使頭髮烏黑亮麗，營養價質甚高。

1 Wash the sausages, cut each into halves lengthwise, then cut into thin slices. Soak black moss until soft and rinse; drain. Soak Chinese black mushrooms until soft, rinse, discard the stems and cut into thick shreds. Trim off the celery ends and leaves and wash, then cut into 1 ¹/₄ " (3 cm) sections.

2 Heat a wok, add 3 T. oil and heat. Stir-fry green onion sections and Chinese black mushrooms until fragrant. Add the sausage slices, stir-fry until dark brown. Add black moss and **1**, stir-fry until the sauce is evaporated completely. Mix in celery, red chili pepper and sesame oil. Serve.

Functions: Rich in protein and iron. May replenish blood. Frequent intake may reduce graying hair.

鮭魚豆腐煲 · Salmon Tofu Casserole

豆腐（2塊）.....................
...... 12兩（450公克）
鮭魚 .. 8兩（300公克）
蒜葉絲 1大匙
鹽 .... $^1/_4$ 小匙

1 ┌ 蔥 4段
    └ 紅辣椒片 1大匙

2 ┌ 高湯 2杯
    │ 味噌 .... 2 $^1/_2$ 大匙
    │ 酒 1大匙
    └ 糖 .... $^1/_2$ 小匙

1 lb. (450 g) ....
.... **2 blocks tofu**
$^2/_3$ lb. (300 g) ...salmon
1 T. .... shredded fresh
garlic spears
$^1/_4$ t. .... salt

1 ┌ 4 sections green on-
    │ ion
    │ 1 T. sliced red chili
    └ pepper

2 ┌ 2 C. stock
    │ 2 $^1/_2$ T. miso
    │ 1 T. cooking wine
    └ $^1/_4$ t. sugar

1 每塊豆腐切成8小塊，入開水煮2分鐘後，盛起瀝乾；
 魚肉去骨亦切同樣大小，入鹽醃約10分鐘。

2 砂鍋熱入油1$^1/_2$大匙燒熱，入魚肉稍煎至淺褐色盛起。

3 砂鍋續入油1大匙燒熱，入**1**料炒香，再入魚肉、豆
 腐及拌勻的**2**料，以大火煮開改小火加蓋燜煮至入味
 （約30分鐘），最後撒上蒜葉絲即可。

 功效：有降血壓、健脾胃、利水消腫、清熱解毒及大補
 氣血之功效。

1 Cut each block of tofu into 8 small squares, scald
 in boiling water for 2 minutes; remove and drain.
 Remove the bones in the salmon and cut into the
 same size pieces; marinate in salt for 10 minutes.

2 Heat a casserole, add 1 $^1/_2$ T. oil and heat. Stir-fry
 salmon pieces until lightly brown. Remove.

3 Add 1 T. oil in the casserole and heat. Stir-fry **1**
 until fragrant. Add salmon, tofu and well-mixed
 2 . Bring it to a boil over high heat. Turn the
 heat to low and simmer, cover with a lid, until
 taste permeates mixture (about 30 minutes).
 Sprinkle on shredded fresh garlic spears and
 serve.

 Functions: May reduce blood pressure and edema,
 and strengthen internal organs. Promotes chi.

洋菇燴甜豆 · Mushrooms and Sugar Snow Peas

新鮮洋菇 １８０公克
甜豆 ... 4兩（１５０公克）

1[蔥 6段
   薑 2片

2[高湯 .... ¹/₄杯
   醬油 .... 1 大匙
   蠔油、酒 ..... 各 1 小匙
   糖 .... ¹/₂小匙
   胡椒粉 .... ¹/₈小匙

3[水 .... 2 小匙
   太白粉 .... ¹/₂小匙

1 洋菇洗淨，入開水中川燙，隨即撈起，漂涼瀝乾；甜豆洗淨，去老纖維，入開水中川燙，隨即撈起漂涼瀝乾。

2 鍋熱入油2大匙燒熱，入**1**料爆香，續入洋菇炒數下，再入**2**料煮開，最後入甜豆及**3**料勾芡即可。

功效：利濕解毒，治水腫腳氣，亦有降血脂、平血壓、利尿等作用。

6 ¹/₃ oz. (180 g) fresh mushrooms
¹/₃ lb. (150 g) .... sugar snow peas

1[6 sections green onion
   2 slices ginger root

2[¹/₄ C. stock
   1 T. soy sauce
   1 t. each: oyster sauce, cooking wine
   ¹/₂ t. sugar
   ¹/₈ t. pepper

3[2 t. water
   ¹/₂ t. cornstarch

1 Wash the mushrooms, parboil in boiling water. Remove and rinse under cold water to cool, drain. Wash the sugar snow peas, remove the tough fiber. Parboil in boiling water, remove and rinse under cold water to cool, drain.

2 Heat a wok, add 2 T. oil and heat. Stir-fry **1** until fragrant. Add mushrooms to fry slightly. Pour in **2** and bring to a boil. Then add sugar snow peas and thicken with **3**. Serve.

Functions: Has a diuretic effect. Lessens edema, cholesterol and blood pressure.

紫菜拌金菇 · Enoki Salad

金針菇（淨重）..................
.... 8兩（３００公克）
紫菜 3張
芹菜末 4大匙

1┌ 醬油 .... 1 ¹/₃ 大匙
  │ 麻油 .... 2 小匙
  └ 米醋 .... 1 ¹/₂ 小匙

1 金針菇洗淨，入開水中川燙，隨即撈起，入冷開水中漂涼；紫菜剪絲備用。

2 金針菇入 **1** 料拌勻盛盤，灑芹菜末，並以紫菜絲圍邊。

功效：含豐富的碘、鐵、維他命Ｂ、Ｃ和膠質，適合高血壓、糖尿病、肥胖者及婦人更年期障礙，顏面易潮紅者食用。

²/₃ lb. (300 g) ...golden mushrooms (net weight)
3 .... nori sheets
4 T. ..... minced celery

1┌ 1 ¹/₃ T. soy sauce
  │ 2 t. sesame oil
  └ 1 ¹/₂ t. rice vinegar

1 Wash golden mushrooms and scald in boiling water; remove immediately, then rinse under cold water to cool. Snip nori sheets into shreds.

2 Mix golden mushrooms with **1**, sprinkle on minced celery and decorate with shredded nori. Serve.

Functions: Rich in iodine, iron, vitamin B, C, and gelatin. Ideal for those with high blood pressure, diabets, obesity, hot flashes and menopause problems.

清炒雙菇 · Double Mushrooms

1
金針菇	九層塔葉 ２０公克
.. ６兩（２２５公克）	薑 ３片
新鮮香菇 １００公克	鹽 .... $^1/_2$小匙
芹菜（淨重）５６公克	

1 金針菇洗淨去頭，香菇洗淨去蒂與薑均切絲；芹菜洗淨切成４公分段；九層塔葉洗淨備用。

2 鍋熱入油１$^1/_2$大匙燒熱，入薑絲炒香，續入**1**料炒熟，再入鹽調味，起鍋前入九層塔葉拌炒均勻即可。

功效：消除疲勞，增強身體抵抗力。

1
$^1/_2$ lb. (225 g) golden mushrooms	$^2/_3$ oz. (20 g) ...... fresh basil leaves
3 $^1/_2$ oz. (100 g) fresh Chinese black mushrooms	3 slices ..... ginger root
2 oz. (56 g) ...celery	$^1/_2$ t. .... salt

1 Wash golden mushrooms and trim off the ends. Wash black mushrooms, remove the stems and shred. Shred ginger roots. Wash the celery and cut into 1 $^1/_2$" (4 cm) sections. Wash basil leaves.

2 Heat a wok, add 1 $^1/_2$ T. oil and heat. Stir-fry shredded ginger roots until fragrant. Add **1** and stir-fry until tender. Season with salt. Mix in basil leaves evenly and serve.

Functions: May reduce fatigue and improve immunity.

香腸炒雙蔬 · Sausages and Vegetables

熟玉米筍4兩（150公克）
台式香腸、四季豆 ....
.... 各3兩（115公克）
蒜末 2小匙

1[水 .... ¹/₂杯
糖、鹽 ..... 各¹/₂小匙
味精 .... ¹/₈小匙

2[水 .... ¹/₂大匙
太白粉 .... ¹/₂小匙

¹/₃ lb. (150 g) ...cooked
baby corn
¹/₄ lb. (115 g) each:
Taiwanese sausages,
string beans
2 t. minced garlic cloves

1[¹/₂ C. water
¹/₂ t. each: salt,
sugar

2[¹/₂ T. water
¹/₂ t. cornstarch

1 香腸洗淨蒸熟切丁；四季豆洗淨去老纖維，與玉米筍均切丁備用。

2 鍋熱入油2大匙燒熱，入香腸煸炒至出油，續入蒜末炒香，再依序入四季豆、玉米筍及**1**料煮開，續煮2分鐘後，以**2**料勾芡拌勻即可。

■ 台式香腸可以臘腸3兩（115公克）代替。

功效：具有通便、整腸及助消化之作用，另外將香腸或臘腸與蔬菜同炒，可防止亞硝胺的形成，故不必擔心吃臘腸或香腸易產生癌症。

1 Wash the sausages, steam until done, then dice. Remove the tough fiber on string beans, wash and dice. Dice baby corn.

2 Heat a wok, add 2 T. oil and heat. Stir-fry diced sausages until fat comes out. Add minced garlic cloves and stir-fry until fragrant. Add string beans, baby corn, and **1**. Bring it to a boil and cook for 2 minutes. Thicken with **2**. Serve.

■ Taiwanese sausages may be replaced by ¹/₄ lb. (115 g) Cantonese sausages.

Functions: May improve digestive organs and bowel movement.

五彩芽菜 · Colorful Sprouts

綠豆芽、紅豆芽各８５公克
雞胸肉絲、胡蘿蔔絲 ....
.... 各５６公克
黃豆芽、黑豆芽各５０公克

1 ⎡ 麻油 .... ¹/₂ 小匙
⎢ 太白粉 .... ¹/₄ 小匙
⎣ 鹽 .... ¹/₈ 小匙

2 ⎡ 蔥 .... 4 段
⎣ 薑 .... 2 片

3 ⎡ 鹽 .... ¹/₄ 小匙
⎣ 味精 .... ¹/₈ 小匙

3 oz. (85 g) each: bean sprouts, red bean sprouts
2 oz. (56 g) each: shredded chicken breast, shredded carrot
1 ³/₄ oz. (50 g) each: soy bean sprouts, black bean sprouts

1 ⎡ ¹/₂ t. sesame oil
⎢ ¹/₄ t. cornstarch
⎣ ¹/₈ t. salt

2 ⎡ 4 sections green onion
⎣ 2 slices ginger root

3 ¹/₄ t. salt

1 綠豆芽、紅豆芽、黃豆芽、黑豆芽等均洗淨去皮；雞胸肉絲入 **1** 料拌醃約１５分鐘後，續入油 ¹/₂ 大匙拌勻；薑切絲備用。

2 鍋熱入油１大匙燒熱，入雞胸肉絲炒至變色盛起。

3 鍋續入油１大匙燒熱，入 **2** 料炒香，續入黃豆芽、黑豆芽、胡蘿蔔絲及水２大匙炒至黃豆芽稍軟，再入雞胸肉、綠豆芽、紅豆芽及 **3** 料拌炒均勻即可。

功效：芽菜甘涼、爽口，適合口乾舌燥者食用，且其具有豐富的蛋白質、維他命與礦物質。

1 Wash bean sprouts, red bean sprouts, soy bean sprouts, black bean sprouts and snip off the ends. Marinate shredded chicken breast in **1** for about 15 minutes. Shred ginger. Add ¹/₂ T. oil and mix well.

2 Heat a wok, add 1 T. oil and heat. Stir-fry shredded chicken until color changes. Remove.

3 Add 1 T. oil in the wok and heat. Stir-fry **2** until fragrant. Stir in soy bean sprouts, black bean sprouts, carrot, and 2 T. water until soy bean sprouts are tender. Add shredded chicken, bean sprouts, red bean sprouts and **3**. Mix well and serve.

Functions: Sprouts are sweet, refreshing and pleasant. Ideal for those with dry mouth and thirst. Rich in protein, vitamins and minerals.

六人份 Serves 6

奶油烤白菜 · Cabbage Au Gratin

大白菜1斤（600公克）
里肌肉 56公克
起司絲 .... ¹/₂杯
洋蔥末、奶水 ..... 各¹/₄杯
麵粉 4大匙
奶油 2大匙

1
水 1杯
鹽 .... ³/₄小匙
糖 .... ¹/₄小匙
味精 .... ¹/₈小匙

1 ¹/₃ lb. (600 g)....nappa cabbage
2 oz. (56 g).....pork loin
¹/₂ C. .... shredded cheese
¹/₄ C. each: minced onions, evaporated milk

4 T. .... flour
2 T. .... butter

1
1 C. water
³/₄ t. salt
¹/₄ t. sugar

1 大白菜洗淨，切4×5公分長段；里肌肉洗淨切1×3.5公分薄片；烤箱預熱至250℃。

2 鍋熱入油2大匙燒熱，入里肌肉炒至變色盛起；鍋續入大白菜拌炒數下，再入**1**料及肉片煮開，改小火煮至菜梗熟軟（約5分鐘），撈起瀝乾，盛於容器內，餘汁取1¹/₂杯留用。

3 鍋熱入奶油燒熱，入洋蔥末炒香，續入麵粉炒勻，再徐徐入白菜湯汁、奶水炒至糊狀即熄火，淋於大白菜上（邊淋邊拌），撒上起司絲，即入烤箱烤至表面呈金黃色（約15分鐘）即可。

功效：本品具有補虛損，益肺胃，生津潤腸之效，對於體虛及常感勞累的人也適合食用。

1 Wash cabbage and cut into 1 ¹/₂" x 2" (4 x 5 cm) long sections. Wash pork loin and cut into ¹/₂" x 1 ³/₈" (1 x 3.5 cm) thin slices. Preheat the oven to 475°F (250°C).

2 Heat a wok, add 2 T. oil and heat. Stir-fry pork slices until color changes; remove. Add cabbage into the wok and stir-fry a while, add **1** and pork. Bring to a boil. Turn the heat to low and simmer until cabbage is tender (about 5 minutes). Remove and drain. Place the cabbage in an oven proof container. Retain one and half of the juice for later use.

3 Heat a wok, add the butter to melt. Stir-fry shredded onions until fragrant. Add the flour to fry. Slowly pour in the cabbage juice and milk until the sauce thickens. Stir the cabbage while pouring on the sauce. Sprinkle on shredded cheese and bake in the preheated oven until golden brown (about 15 minutes). Serve.

Functions: May reduce fatigue and improve strength.

63

百合炒菠菜 · Lily Bulbs and Spinach

菠菜 ... 9兩（３４０公克）
新鮮百合３兩（１１５公克）

1⌈ 水 ２大匙
   │ 鹽 .... ³/₄ 小匙
   └ 味精 .... ¹/₄ 小匙

1 菠菜去頭洗淨切３公分長段；百合一瓣瓣剝開洗淨，瀝乾備用。

2 鍋熱入油２大匙燒熱，入百合拌炒數下，續入菠菜及 **1** 料炒至菠菜熟即可。

功效：有潤肺止咳，補充元氣之功效。

³/₄ lb. (340 g)....spinach
¹/₄ lb. (115 g) .... fresh
lily bulbs

1⌈ 2 T. water
   └ ³/₄ t. salt

1 Trim off the spinach ends, wash and cut into $1\frac{1}{4}$" (3 cm) sections. Peel off each lily bulbs petals, wash and pat dry.

2 Heat a wok, add 2 T. oil and heat. Stir-fry lily bulb petals slightly. Add spinach and **1** to fry until tender. Serve.

Functions: May soothe the lung and reduce coughing.

竹笙燴白果 · Gingko Nuts and Dictyophora

青江菜6兩（225公克）
白果罐頭（去汁）90公克
竹笙 20公克

1
素高湯 .... $^1/_2$ 杯
酒 .... 1 小匙
鹽、糖 ..... 各$^3/_8$ 小匙
味精 .... $^1/_8$ 小匙

2
水 .... 2 小匙
太白粉 .... 1 小匙

3
素高湯 .... $^1/_4$ 杯
麻油 .... $^1/_2$ 小匙
鹽、糖 ..... 各$^1/_4$ 小匙

1 竹笙泡軟洗淨切3公分段，與白果均入開水中川燙，撈
起瀝乾。

2 青江菜洗淨，直切成兩半，入開水中川燙，撈起漂涼瀝
乾，圍邊盤飾。

3 鍋熱入油1$^1/_2$大匙燒熱，入竹笙及**1**料煮至入味（約
2分鐘），再以**2**料勾芡，盛起置盤上。

4 鍋續入白果及**3**料煮至湯汁收乾，盛起置竹笙上即可。

素高湯作法：黃豆芽200公克洗淨，加水2杯入鍋
中煮開後，改小火慢熬，待湯汁剩1杯時去渣，取湯汁
即為素高湯。

功效：對於小孩子氣管弱易咳嗽，婦人體虛白帶多及頻
尿者有良好之功效。

$^1/_2$ lb. (225 g) bok choy
3 $^1/_4$ oz. (90 g) canned gingko nuts (drain)
$^2/_3$ oz. (20 g) .... net bearing dictyophora

1
$^1/_2$ C. vegetarian stock
1 t. cooking wine
$^3/_8$ t. each: sugar, salt

2
2 t. water
1 t. cornstarch

3
$^1/_4$ C. vegetarian stock
$^1/_2$ t. sesame oil
$^1/_4$ t. each: sugar, salt

1 Soak and wash net bearing dictyophora in water until soft and cut into 1 $^1/_4$" (3 cm) long sections. Scald net bearing dictyophora and gingko nuts in boiling water, drain.

2 Wash bok choy and cut into halves lengthwise. Scald in boiling water and rinse under cold water to cool, drain. Circle a plate with bok choy.

3 Heat a wok, add 1 $^1/_2$ T. oil and heat. Add net bearing dictyophora and **1** until taste permeates mixture (about 2 minutes). Thicken with **2**. Remove and place on the plate.

4 Add gingko nuts and **3** into the wok. Cook until the sauce has evaporated. Remove and place on top of the net bearing dictyophora. Serve.

Vegetarian Stock : Wash 7 oz. (200 g) soy bean sprouts and add 2 C. water. Bring to a boil. Turn the heat to low and simmer until the soup reduces to 1 C. Sieve off the dregs. The clear soup is the vegetarian stock.

Functions: May improve respiratory functions for children, and urine frequency for women.

什錦蒟蒻絲 · Diet Special

蒟蒻絲（淨重）................
.... 8兩（３００公克）
雞胸肉 １３０公克
芹菜 ８５公克
胡蘿蔔絲 ５６公克

1
酒 .... ¹/₂ 大匙
太白粉 １小匙
鹽 .... ¹/₄ 小匙

2
香菇絲 .... ¹/₃ 杯
薑末 .... ¹/₂ 大匙

3
水 .... ²/₃ 杯
醬油、黑醋 .. 各１大匙
酒 .... ¹/₂ 大匙
糖 １小匙
胡椒粉、味精各¹/₄ 小匙

2/₃ lb. (300 g) shredded shirataki
4 ¹/₂ oz. (130 g) chicken breast
3 oz. (85 g) .... celery
2 oz. (56 g) .. shredded carrot

1
¹/₂ T. cooking wine
1 t. cornstarch
¹/₄ t. salt

2
¹/₃ C. shredded Chinese black mushrooms
¹/₂ T. shredded ginger roots

3
²/₃ C. water
1 T. each: soy sauce, black vinegar
¹/₂ T. cooking wine
1 t. sugar
¹/₄ t. pepper

1 蒟蒻絲入開水中煮５分鐘，撈起漂涼瀝乾，切４公分長段；雞胸肉洗淨切絲，入**1**料拌醃１０分鐘後，入油１大匙拌勻；芹菜去根及葉洗淨切３公分長段，再稍拍扁備用。

2 鍋熱入油２大匙燒熱，入雞絲炒至變色，盛起備用。

3 另鍋熱入油２大匙燒熱，入**2**料爆香，續入胡蘿蔔絲及蒟蒻絲炒勻，再入**3**料煮開，改小火再煮約５分鐘，最後入雞絲及芹菜炒勻即可。

功效：本品具有降血壓及通便整腸、減肥之功效。

1 Boil shirataki in boiling water for 5 minutes, remove and rinse under cold water to cool; drain and cut into 1 ¹/₂" (4 cm) long sections. Shred the chicken breast and marinate in **1** for 10 minutes; mix in 1 T. oil and mix well. Trim off the celery ends and leaves; wash and cut into 1 ¹/₄" (3 cm) long sections.

2 Heat a wok, add 2 T. oil and heat. Stir-fry shredded chicken until color changes. Remove.

3 Heat another wok, add 2 T. oil and heat. Stir-fry **2** until fragrant. Add carrot and shirataki; mix well. Add **3** and bring to a boil. Turn the heat to low and simmer for 5 minutes. Add chicken and celery. Mix well and serve.

Functions: May improve blood pressure and bowel movement.

66

蒟蒻蘆筍 · Asparagus and Shirataki

蒟蒻（1塊）...180公克
蘆筍4兩....（150公克）
熟草菇3兩（115公克）
薑...........................4片

1┌ 水 .... 2 大匙
  │ 蠔油、酒 各1大匙
  └ 鹽、糖 ..... 各 $^1/_2$ 小匙

2┌ 水 .... 1 大匙
  └ 太白粉 .... $^1/_2$ 小匙

6 $^1/_3$ oz. (180 g) ....
shirataki
$^1/_3$ lb. (150 g) asparagus
$^1/_4$ lb. (115 g) ....
boiled or canned straw
mushrooms
4 slices .... ginger root

1┌ 2 T. water
  │ 1 T. each: oyster
  │ sauce, cooking wine
  │ $^1/_2$ t. each: salt,
  └ sugar

2┌ 1 T. water
  └ $^1/_2$ t. cornstarch

1 蒟蒻切6×1.5公分薄片，中間劃一刀，翻轉捲成麻花狀，入開水中煮5分鐘去鹼味，撈起漂涼瀝乾；蘆筍去老纖維，洗淨切3公分長段，入開水中川燙，撈起漂涼瀝乾；熟草菇切半備用。

2 鍋熱入油2大匙燒熱，入薑片爆香，入蒟蒻拌炒數下，續入蘆筍及草菇炒勻，再入**1**料調味，最後以**2**料勾芡即可。

功效：具通便整腸，抗癌保健之功效，適合高血脂、便秘及肥胖者食用。

1 Cut shirataki into 2 $^1/_2$" x $^5/_8$" (6 x 1.5 cm) thin slices, cut a slit in the center. Pull one end through the slit to form a twisted center. Cook in boiling water for 5 minutes to get rid off the salty taste. Rinse under cold water and drain. Remove tough fibers off the asparagus, wash and cut into 1 $^1/_4$" (3 cm) long sections; scald in boiling water, remove and rinse under cold water, drain. Cut each straw mushroom in half.

2 Heat a wok, add 2 T. oil and heat. Stir-fry ginger slices until fragrant. Add shirataki and fry slightly. Add asparagus and mushrooms, stir-fry and mix well. Season with **1** and thicken with **2**. Serve.

Functions: May regulate better bowel and intestine movements. A good dish for those having high cholesterol, constipation and obesity.

蘆筍炒三絲 ▪ Chicken and Asparagus

雞胸肉4兩（１５０公克）
蘆筍（淨重）　１３０公克
熟筍絲、胡蘿蔔絲 ....
.... 各2兩（７５公克）

2 ┌ 蔥末 .... 1 大匙
　└ 薑末 .... 1 小匙

3 ┌ 酒 .... 1 小匙
　├ 鹽、糖 ..... 各 $^1/_2$ 小匙
　└ 味精 .... $^1/_8$ 小匙

1 ┌ 水 .... 1 大匙
　├ 太白粉 .... $^1/_2$ 大匙
　├ 酒 .... 1 小匙
　├ 鹽 .... $^1/_4$ 小匙
　└ 胡椒粉 .... $^1/_8$ 小匙

$^1/_3$ lb. (150 g)...chicken breast
$4\,^1/_2$ oz. (130 g) asparagus (net weight)
$2\,^1/_2$ oz. (75 g)each: shredded boiled bamboo shoots, shredded carrot

2 ┌ 1 T. minced green onion
　└ 1 t. minced ginger roots

3 ┌ 1 t. cooking wine
　└ $^1/_2$ t. each: sugar, salt

1 ┌ 1 T. water
　├ $^1/_2$ T. cornstarch
　├ 1 t. cooking wine
　├ $^1/_4$ t. salt
　└ $^1/_8$ t. pepper

1 雞胸肉洗淨切絲，入 **1** 料拌醃１０分鐘，續入油１大匙拌勻；蘆筍洗淨切斜段。

2 鍋熱入油２大匙燒熱，入雞絲炒至變色盛起。

3 鍋續入油１大匙燒熱，入 **2** 料爆香，續入胡蘿蔔絲炒軟，再入蘆筍、熟筍絲及雞絲炒勻，最後以 **3** 料調味。

功效：含有豐富的維他命Ｃ和纖維質，能清涼退火，降血壓及預防動脈硬化，具有抗癌、抗菌之功效。

1 Wash chicken breast and shred; marinate in **1** for 10 minutes, then add 1 T. oil and mix well. Wash asparagus and cut into slanting sections.

2 Heat a wok, add 2 T. oil and heat. Stir-fry shredded chicken until color changes. Remove immediately.

3 Add 1 T. oil to the wok and heat. Stir-fry **2** until fragrant. Add shredded carrot and fry until tender. Add asparagus, boiled bamboo shoots and chicken to fry and mix well. Season with **3** and serve.

Functions: Rich in vitamin C and fiber. May reduce inner heat and improve blood pressure. May prevent hardening of the arteries.

干貝絲瓜 · Sing Qua and Dried Scallops

澎湖絲瓜(淨重)565公克	
濕木耳 85公克	
胡蘿蔔 50公克	
干貝 2個	
蔥 5段	

1
水 2大匙
酒 .... $^1/_2$大匙
鹽 1小匙
麻油 .... $^1/_2$小匙
胡椒粉、味精各$^1/_4$小匙

2
水 1大匙
太白粉 2小匙

1 干貝稍沖洗，加水2大匙，入鍋蒸軟（約20分鐘），趁熱撕成細絲，蒸汁留用。

2 絲瓜切成4公分段，再切成長片狀；木耳洗淨去蒂切2×4公分薄片；胡蘿蔔洗淨去皮切同樣大小片狀。

3 鍋熱入油2大匙燒熱，入蔥炒香，續入胡蘿蔔略炒，再入干貝、蒸汁、木耳、**1**料及絲瓜，以小火煮至絲瓜熟透（約3分鐘），最後以**2**料勾芡即可。

功效：含有豐富的蛋白質，維他命A、B、C及鐵質等，有解毒、清熱、健胃、祛痰及美化肌膚之功效。

1 $^3/_4$ lb. (565 g) ... Sing Qua (net weight)
3 oz. (85 g) ..... soaked black wood ears
1 $^3/_4$ oz. (50 g) .. carrot
2 .... dried scallops
5 sections green onion

1
- 2 T. water
- $^1/_2$ T. cooking wine
- 1 t. salt
- $^1/_2$ t. sesame oil
- $^1/_4$ t. pepper

2
- 1 T. water
- 2 t. cornstarch

1 Wash the dried scallops, add 2 T. water and steam until soft (about 20 minutes). Tear to shreds while still warm. Keep the juice for later use.

2 Cut Sing Qua into 1 $^1/_2$" (4 cm) sections, then slice. Wash wood ears, discard the tough ends and cut into $^3/_4$" x 1 $^1/_2$" (2 x 4 cm) slices. Wash carrot, pare off the skin and cut into same size slices.

3 Heat a wok, add 2 T. oil and heat. Stir-fry green onion until fragrant. Add carrot slices to fry slightly. Add scallop shreds, steam juice, wood ear slices, **1** and Sing Qua to cook over low heat until Sing Qua strips are tender (about 3 minutes). Thicken with **2** and serve.

Functions: Rich in protein, vitamins A, B, C, and iron. May promote anti-toxins and improve skin.

五味苦瓜 · Bitter Melon Salad

苦瓜（淨重）................
.... 9兩（３４０公克）

1┌冷開水 4杯
  └鹽.................. ¹/₂大匙

2┌醬油 3大匙
  │蔥末 2大匙
  │糖 .... 1 ¹/₂大匙
  │蒜末、香菜末各１大匙
  │薑末、紅辣椒末 ....
  │........... 各¹/₂大匙
  │米醋 2小匙
  └味精 .... ¹/₈小匙

³/₄ lb. (340 g) ... bitter
melon (net weight)

1┌4 C. cold water
  └¹/₂ T. salt

2┌3 T. soy sauce
  │2 T. minced green
  │onion
  │1 ¹/₂ T. sugar
  │1 T. each: minced
  │garlic cloves, minced
  │coriander
  │¹/₂ T. each: minced
  │ginger roots, minced
  │red chili pepper
  └2 t. rice vinegar

1 苦瓜切薄片，入**1**料浸泡後直接放入冰箱冷藏，待吃時再撈起瀝乾，置盤備用。

2 **2**料拌勻，淋於苦瓜上即可。

功效：具有清暑熱，明目、通便之功效，對於因炎熱而產生之頭昏、頭脹、目赤及便秘者，可多食用。

1 Cut bitter melon into thin slices, soak in **1** and refrigerate until ready to serve.

2 Mix **2** well and pour over bitter melon slices. Serve.

Functions: An ideal summer dish for soothing the body, sharpening the eyes, reduces constipation and dizziness due to heat.

苦瓜炒魚乾 · Dried Small Fish and Bitter Melon

苦瓜 1 條（淨重）.............
.... 9 兩（３４０公克）

小魚乾 ２０公克

1 ┌ 豆豉 .... 1 大匙
└ 蒜末、辣椒末各 1 小匙

2 ┌ 高湯 .... $^1/_2$ 杯
│ 醬油 .... 1 大匙
│ 酒、糖 ..... 各 $^1/_2$ 大匙
│ 太白粉 .... $^1/_2$ 小匙
└ 味精 .... $^1/_4$ 小匙

$^3/_4$ lb. (340 g) ... bitter melon (net weight)
$^2/_3$ oz. (20 g) ...... dried small fish

1 ┌ 1 T. fermented black beans
│ 1 t. each: minced garlic cloves, minced
└ red chili pepper

2 ┌ $^1/_2$ C. stock
│ 1 T. soy sauce
│ $^1/_2$ T. each: cooking wine, sugar
└ $^1/_2$ t. cornstarch

1 苦瓜洗淨切薄片，泡鹽水（水 4 杯加鹽 1 小匙）以去部分苦味，小魚乾稍沖洗泡軟，瀝乾備用。

2 鍋熱入油 2 大匙燒熱，入小魚乾及 **1** 料炒香，續入苦瓜煸炒至變色，再入 **2** 料煮開，改小火續炒至苦瓜稍軟即可。

功效：對口苦咽乾、火氣旺、食慾不佳、多夢難眠、極易長青春痘者，有很好之抒解作用。

1 Wash bitter melon and cut into thin slices; soak in brine (1t. salt and 4 C. water) to reduce bitterness. Rinse dried small fish and soak in water until soft, drain and pat dry.

2 Heat a wok, add 2 T. oil and heat. Stir-fry small fish and **1** until fragrant. Add bitter melon and stir-fry until color changes. Pour in **2** and bring to a boil. Turn the heat to low and continuously stir-fry until bitter melon is tender. Serve.

Functions: May relieve dry mouth and thirst. May improve appetite, sleep quality, and reduce acne.

蒸茄段 · Steamed Eggplants

茄子 ... 9兩（３４０公克）
蔥花 ２大匙

1
醬油 ２大匙
麻油、蒜末 .. 各１大匙
芝麻醬 ２小匙
糖 .... 1 $^1/_4$ 小匙
花生醬、米醋、辣油 ..
.... 各１小匙

$^3/_4$ lb. (340 g) eggplants
2 T. .... chopped green onions

2
2 T. soy sauce
1 T. each: sesame oil, minced garlic cloves
2 t. sesame paste
1 $^1/_4$ t. sugar
1 t. each: peanut butter, rice vinegar, chili oil

1 茄子去蒂洗淨直切成兩半，在表皮上劃花刀，再切６公分長段，排盤備用。

2 茄子入蒸鍋以大火蒸軟（約１５分鐘），取出放涼瀝乾，淋上拌勻之 **1** 料，再撒上蔥花即可。

功效：茄子含有豐富的維他命Ａ、Ｂ、Ｐ、蛋白質、醣類及礦物質，對於老年人、糖尿病、病後恢復期之患者，有輔助食療之效。

1 Trim off the eggplant ends, wash and cut each in two lengthwise. Score diamonds on the skin. Then cut into 2 $^1/_2$ " (6 cm) sections.

2 Steam the eggplant over high heat until tender (about 15 minutes). Remove and leave to cool. Pour on well-mixed **1** sauce. Sprinkle on chopped green onion and serve.

Functions: Eggplant is rich with vitamins A, B, P, protein, carbohydrates, and minerals. A good dish for the elderly, diabetics, and those recovering from illness.

紅燒薯塊 · Braised Potatoes

馬鈴薯1斤（600公克）	**1**⌈ 蔥 .... 5 段	1 ¹/₃ lb. (600 g) potatoes	**1**⌈ 5 sections green	
九層塔葉 56公克	└ 薑 .... 4 片	2 oz. (56 g) basil leaves		onion
麻油 .... 1 小匙		1 t. .... sesame oil	└ 4 slices ginger root	
	2⌈ 水 .... 1 杯		**2**⌈ 1 C. water	
	│ 醬油 .... 2 ¹/₃ 大匙		│ 2 ¹/₃ T. soy sauce	
	└ 糖 .... 1 小匙		└ 1 t. sugar	

1　馬鈴薯洗淨去皮切滾刀塊後泡水，煮時再瀝乾水份；九層塔葉洗淨備用。

2　鍋熱入油2大匙燒熱，入**1**料爆香，續入馬鈴薯煸炒至表面微黃，再入**2**料煮開，改小火加蓋燜煮至湯汁快收乾（每隔5分鐘翻面一次，以免焦底），最後入九層塔葉及麻油炒勻即可。

　　功效：補虛強身，適合老年人及胃腸較弱者食用。

1　Wash and pare the potatoes, cut into diagonal pieces. Soak in water to prevent discoloring. Drain prior to cooking. Wash the basil leaves.

2　Heat a wok, add 2 T. oil and heat. Stir-fry **1** until fragrant. Add the potatoes and fry until slightly brown on the surfaces. Add **2** and bring to a boil. Turn the heat to low and simmer covered until the sauce is nearly all evaporated. (turn every 5 minutes to prevent burning). Mix in basil leaves and sesame oil. Serve.

Functions: May improve strength. Ideal for the elderly and those with weak digestive systems.

黃豆糙米飯 · Brown Rice with Soy Beans

糙米 .... 2杯　　黃豆 .... $^1/_2$杯

2 C. .... brown rice　　$^1/_2$ **C. .... soy beans**

1 黃豆洗淨，加水浸泡4小時備用。

2 糙米洗淨，加黃豆及水2杯入電鍋，外鍋加水3杯，煮至熟透即可。

　功效：含有豐富的維他命B群、E、K和纖維質等，有防止便秘、貧血、老化之作用。

1 Wash soy beans and soak in water for 4 hours.

2 Wash brown rice. Add brown rice, soy beans and 2 C. water into the inner pot of a rice cooker. Add 3 C. water into the outer pot and cook until done.

Functions: Rich in vitamins B complex, E, K, and fiber. May prevent constipation, anemia and show down aging.

糙米香炒飯 · Fried Soy Brown Rice

黃豆糙米飯 ....
.... 1斤（600公克）
洋火腿丁、熟青豆仁 ....
.... 各¹/₂杯
熟胡蘿蔔丁 .... ¹/₃杯

1┌ 香菇丁 3大匙
 └ 蔥末 1大匙

2┌ 鹽 .... ³/₄小匙
 └ 味精 .... ¹/₄小匙

1 鍋熱入油2 ¹/₂大匙燒熱，入**1**料炒香，續入火腿及胡
  蘿蔔拌炒數下，再依序入黃豆糙米飯、熟青豆仁及**2**料
  炒勻即可。

■ 黃豆糙米飯煮法請參見第74頁。

功效：含豐富的維他命B1，具有防止便秘、貧血、腳
氣病及老化之作用，且有美化肌膚之功效。

---

1 ¹/₃ lb. (600 g) brown rice with soy beans
¹/₂ C. each: diced ham, boiled green peas
¹/₃ C. .... boiled and diced carrot

1┌ 3 T. diced Chinese black mushrooms
 │ 1 T. minced green
 └ onion

2 ³/₄ t. salt

1 Heat a wok, add 2 ¹/₂ T. oil and heat. Stir-fry **1** until fragrant. Add diced ham and diced carrot to fry. Add brown rice with soy beans, boiled green peas, and season with salt. Stir and heat well. Serve.

■ Please refer to page 74 for brown rice with soy beans.

Functions: Rich in vitamin B1. May prevent constipation, anemia, beriberi and show the aging process.

核果排骨粥 · Nuts and Pork Congee

1
- 蓬萊米 .... 1 杯
- 核桃、栗子、蓮子 ......
  .... 各 $^1/_4$ 杯
- 松子 .... $^1/_8$ 杯

小排骨8兩（300公克）

2
- 鹽 .... 1 $^1/_4$ 小匙
- 味精 .... $^1/_4$ 小匙

1
- 1 C. Japanese rice (round rice)
- $^1/_4$ C. each: lotus seeds, chestnuts, walnuts
- $^1/_8$ C. pine nuts

$^2/_3$ lb. (300 g) spare ribs

2 1 $^1/_4$ t. salt

1 小排骨洗淨，入開水中川燙，隨即撈起瀝乾；栗子洗淨泡水1小時，以牙籤挑去殘留外殼，其餘 **1** 料亦洗淨。

2 鍋內入排骨、**1** 料及水10杯，以大火煮開，改小火煮至熟爛（約70分鐘），其間每隔5分鐘攪動一次，以免焦底，再以 **2** 料調味即可。

功效：含有豐富的蛋白質、維他命、纖維質和鈣質，營養價值很高，能預防鈣質流失，促進骨骼發育及改善虛弱體質。

1 Wash the ribs, scald in boiling water ; remove and drain. Wash chestnuts and soak in water for one hour; remove the outer film carefully with a toothpick. Wash the rest of the ingredients in **1**.

2 Bring spare ribs, **1** and 10 C. water to a boil over high heat. Turn the heat to low and simmer until tender (about 70 minutes). Stir every 5 minutes to prevent sticking at the bottom. Season with salt. Serve.

Functions: Rich in Protein, vitamins, fiber and calcium. May promote bone development and strengthen weakened body.

香菇雞煲飯 · Chicken Rice Casserole

去骨雞腿 ....
.... 8兩（300公克）
濕木耳 85公克
香菇（8朵）..... 10公克
蓬萊米 .... 1 $^1/_2$ 杯

2
油..................... 1 大匙
醬油 .... 2 小匙
鹽、味精 各$^1/_4$ 小匙

3
蔥..................... 1 枝
嫩薑絲 .... 2 大匙

1
薑 .... 6 片
醬油 ...... 1 $^1/_2$ 大匙
酒 .... 1 大匙
糖 .... 1 小匙

$^2/_3$ lb. (300 g) ....
...boneless chicken leg
3 oz. (85 g) ..... soaked
black wood ears
$^1/_3$ oz. (10 g) 8 Chinese
black mushrooms
1 $^1/_2$ C. Japanese rice
(round rice)

1
6 slices ginger root
1 $^1/_2$ T. soy sauce
1 T. cooking wine
1 t. sugar

2
1 T. oil
2 t. soy sauce
$^1/_4$ t. salt

3
1 stalk green onion
2 T. shredded baby
ginger roots

1 雞腿洗淨；木耳洗淨去蒂切片，將雞腿、木耳及 **1** 料拌醃約30分鐘；香菇洗淨泡軟去蒂切半，煮前再入 **1** 料內拌勻；蔥洗淨切絲，泡水至捲起後，隨即瀝乾。

2 米洗淨瀝乾，入砂鍋加水 1 $^3/_4$ 杯，續入 **2** 料及剩餘之 **1** 料醃汁拌勻，以大火煮開，改小火續煮並不斷攪動至湯汁快收乾，再擺上醃好之材料，加蓋燜煮30分鐘，熄火續燜20分鐘即可。

3 食前將雞腿取出切片，再放回煲飯上，並灑上 **3** 料。

功效：具有防癌，增加免疫力及補充營養之功效。

1 Wash chicken leg and wood ears, discard stems and slice. Marinate chicken leg and wood ears in **1** for 30 minutes. Soak black mushrooms in water until soft, remove stems and cut into halves. Mix the mushrooms into **1** before cooking. Wash green onion and shred; soak in water until curled up, drain.

2 Rinse rice and place in a casserole, add 1 $^3/_4$ C. water, **2** and rest of **1**; mix well. Bring to a boil over high heat. Simmer over low heat until liquid evaporates. Arrange marinated chicken, wood ears and mushroom pieces at top of rice. Cover with a lid and simmer for 30 minutes. Turn heat off and let casserole stand for 20 minutes.

3 Slice the chicken leg and place back in the casserole. Sprinkle on **3** and serve.

Functions: Nutritious and may improve immunity.

長青糕 · Evergreen Cake

麵粉、八寶核果、即食燕　　黑糖 5大匙
麥片 各1杯

1　八寶核果稍沖洗備用。

2　將所有材料混合均勻，再入水1杯調勻成濃稠狀。

3　模型底部抹油（約1大匙），入作法2材料，再入蒸鍋
　　蒸至熟透（約30分鐘）即可。

■ 八寶核果，如松子、核桃、葡萄乾、葵瓜子、南瓜子、
　　腰果、枸杞子、芝麻等，可依個人喜好隨意取代，但因
　　核果類多為高蛋白、高核酸、高普林食品，痛風病患不
　　宜食用太多，偶而食用，有益健康。

　功效：含豐富的維他命B群、礦物質、纖維質和植物蛋
　白，可增強身體抵抗力及防止老人習慣性便秘。

1 C. each: flour, eight-treasure nuts, instant oatmeal　　**5 T. .... brown sugar**

1　Rinse all the nuts.

2　Mix all the ingredients together. Add 1 C. water and mix into a thick paste.

3　Grease the bottom of a cake pan (about 1 T.). Pour in the paste mixture. Steam until done (about 30 minutes). Serve.

■ Eight-treasure nuts may include pine nuts, walnuts, raisins, sunflower seeds, pumpkin seeds, cashew nuts, lycium berries, or sesame seeds. May be replaced depending on individual preference. Nuts contain high levels of protein, nucleic acid, and purine. Gout patients should limit their intake. Occasional intake is good for the health.

Functions: Rich in vitamin B complex, mineral, fiber and vegetable protein. May strengthen immunity and reduce habitual constipation in the elderly.

簡易南瓜派 · Simple Pumpkin Pie

南瓜12兩（450公克）	吐司 12片	**1 lb. (450 g)...pumpkin**	**12 slices .... bread**
地瓜、起司絲	細糖 4大匙	**$1/_2$ lb. (225 g) each:**	**4 T. .... sugar**
..... 各6兩（225公克）		**sweet potatoes, shred-**	
		ded cheese	

1 南瓜洗淨去皮、籽及瓜囊後切薄片；地瓜洗淨去皮切薄片，烤箱預熱至200℃。

2 南瓜及地瓜入蒸鍋蒸至熟爛（約20分鐘），取出壓成泥再入糖拌勻，即為內餡，與起司絲均分成12等份。

3 取1片吐司，抹上1份內餡，再撒上1份起司絲，其餘依序做完，入烤箱上層烤至起司絲呈金黃色即可。

功效：南瓜具有豐富的維他命A、C、E及B群，除能補充營養，且可維持腦和神經細胞的正常發展及延緩老化作用。

1 Wash and pare the pumpkin, discard the seeds and cut meat into thin slices. Wash and pare the sweet potatoes, then cut into thin slices. Preheat the oven to 400°F (200°C).

2 Steam the pumpkin and sweet potatoes until tender (about 20 minutes). Remove. Mash both and mix with sugar for filling. Divide both filling and shredded cheese into 12 equal portions.

3 Spread a layer of the pumpkin filling on each slice of bread. Sprinkle on cheese. Bake in the oven until golden brown.

Functions: Pumpkin is rich with vitamins A, C, E, and B complex. Besides being nutritious, it can also help to maintain normal neurological development and delay aging process.

益壽春捲 · Delightful Fruit Rolls

香蕉（淨重）.....................
.... 8兩（３００公克）
蘋果（淨重）.....................
.... 6兩（２２５公克）
春捲皮 6張

黑芝麻粉 4大匙
糖粉 2大匙

1 麵粉、水 各2大匙

$^2/_3$ lb. (300 g) ....
...bananas (net weight)
$^1/_2$ lb. (225 g) ....
.... apples (net weight)
6 sheets ...egg roll skin

4 T. .... black
sesame powder
2 T. .. powdered sugar

1 2 T. each: flour,
water

1 香蕉、蘋果均切小丁，入黑芝麻粉拌勻即為內餡，均分
成6等份；**1**料調勻成麵糊備用。

2 每張春捲皮中間置1份內餡，包成１２公分長圓筒狀，
接口處以**1**料黏住。

3 平底鍋熱入油５大匙燒熱，入春捲煎至表面呈淺褐色，
取出盛盤，撒上糖粉即可。

功效：含有豐富的維他命Ｃ、纖維質及鉀，能增加腸
胃的蠕動及排除體內毒素，故有幫助消化及美化肌膚
之功效。

1 Dice both bananas and apples. Mix the fruit with black sesame powder to make the filling. Divide it into 6 equal portions. Mix **1** evenly into a paste.

2 Place one fruit filling onto one egg roll skin. Roll it up as a cylinder. Seal the ends with **1** paste.

3 Heat a pan, add 5 T. oil and heat. Fry the rolls until light brown on both sides. Remove to a plate. Sprinkle on powdered sugar and serve.

Functions: High in vitamin C, fiber and potassium. May improve intestine function.

加味四神湯 · Pork and Chinese Herb Soup

小排骨8兩（３００公克）

2┌ 酒 .... 1 大匙
  │ 鹽 .... ¹/₂ 小匙
  └ 味精 .... ¹/₈ 小匙

1┌ 百合、蓮子、山藥 ....
  │ .... 各¹/₄杯
  │ 芡實、薏苡仁 ....
  │ .... 各 2¹/₂大匙
  └ 茯苓（剁碎）.. 1 大匙

1 百合、芡實、薏苡仁稍沖洗，加水浸泡４小時後，撈起
  瀝乾；小排骨洗淨，入開水中川燙，撈起洗淨瀝乾。

2 鍋內入小排骨、**1**料及水１２杯，以大火煮開，改小火
  燜煮至熟爛（約１小時２０分鐘），再以**2**料調味。

  功效：有開胃、助消化、健脾止瀉等功效，對於小孩食
  慾不振，容易腹脹、泄瀉有很好的療效。

²/₃ lb. (300 g) spare ribs

2┌ 1 T. cooking wine
  └ ¹/₂ t. salt

1┌ ¹/₄ C. each: lily bulbs,
  │   lotus seeds, Chinese
  │   yam
  │ 2 ¹/₂ T. each: euryale
  │   seeds, coix seeds
  │ 1 T. poria (chopped
  └ fine)

1 Rinse dried lily bulbs, euryle seeds and coix seeds,
  soak in water for 4 hours; drain. Wash pork ribs
  and scald in boiling water, remove and rinse;
  drain.

2 Bring spare ribs, **1** and 12 C. water to a boil over
  high heat. Turn the heat to low and simmer until
  tender (about 1 hour and 20 minutes). Season
  with **2**. Serve.

  Functions: May promote appetite and relieve
  diarrhea.

山藥蛤蜊燉雞 · Steamed Clams and Chicken

生山藥１２兩（４５０公克）
雞腿 .. ９兩（３４０公克）
蛤蜊 .. ８兩（３００公克）
薑 ４片

**1**
水 ４杯
酒 １大匙
鹽 .... $^3/_4$ 小匙
味精 .... $^1/_4$ 小匙

1 lb. (450 g) ...... fresh
Chinese yam
$^3/_4$ lb. (340 g) ..chicken
leg
$^2/_3$ lb. (300 g) .... clams
4 slices ..... ginger root

1
4 C. water
1 T. cooking wine
$^3/_4$ t. salt

1 蛤蜊泡水吐沙洗淨；山藥洗淨，去皮切滾刀塊；雞腿洗淨剁塊，入開水中川燙，撈起漂涼，瀝乾備用。

2 所有材料及**1**料入燉盅並加蓋，入蒸鍋以大火蒸１小時即可。

功效：對於經常感冒，易腹瀉的人，具有改善體質之作用；又山藥能降血糖，很適合糖尿病者食用。

1 Soak clams in water to get rid of sand and wash. Wash Chinese yam, rinse and pare off the skin; cut into diagonal pieces. Wash chicken leg and chop into serving pieces, scald in boiling water; drain.

2 Place all the ingredients and **1** into a steam pot, cover with a lid. Steam in a steamer over high heat for 1 hour. Serve.

Functions: May improve body strength. Chinese yam may reduce blood sugar, which is good for diabetics.

蒜頭燉雞湯 · Garlic Chicken Soup

全雞2斤（１２００）公克
蒜頭 ...... 2兩（７５公克）

1
┌ 水 .... 4 $^1/_2$ 杯
│ 酒 .... 3 大匙
└ 鹽 .... 1 $^1/_2$ 小匙

2 $^2/_3$ lb. (1200 g) ... one chicken
2 $^1/_2$ oz. (75 g) ... garlic cloves

1
┌ 4 $^1/_2$ C. water
│ 3 T. cooking wine
└ 1 $^1/_2$ t. salt

1 雞洗淨入開水中川燙，撈起漂涼洗淨；蒜頭洗淨去頭及膜，將 $^1/_2$ 之蒜頭塞入雞腹內備用。

2 燉盅入雞、剩餘之 $^1/_2$ 蒜頭及 **1** 料，加盅蓋，再入蒸鍋蒸至雞熟爛（約１小時４０分鐘）即可。

　功效：能除風邪寒痰、溫暖脾胃，在冬季來臨時多食用，可預防流行性感冒，有補充體力之作用。

1 Wash chicken, scald in boiling water; remove and rinse under cold water. Wash garlic cloves, trim off the ends and remove the skins. Stuff the chicken with half of the garlic cloves.

2 Place the chicken, the rest of the garlic cloves, and **1** in a steam pot, cover with a lid and steam in a steamer until tender (about one hour and 40 minutes). Serve.

Functions: May promote inner heat, a good winter dish to ward off colds.

紅棗鱸魚湯 · Jujube and Bass Soup

鱸魚（1條）....................
.....１２兩（４５０公克）
紅棗 8個
老薑 4片
九層塔葉 .... $^1/_4$ 杯

1 ⌈ 酒 .... 1 小匙
│ 鹽 .... $^1/_2$ 小匙
└ 味精 .... $^1/_8$ 小匙

1 鱸魚去鰓及內臟洗淨，橫切成兩段，紅棗洗淨去籽。

2 鍋內入薑片、紅棗及水７杯，以大火煮開，改小火燜煮至湯汁剩約４杯，入鱸魚以中火煮至熟透（約１０分鐘），再加 **1** 料調味，並撒上九層塔葉即可。

功效：對受風寒所引起的鼻塞、流鼻水具有改善作用，且適合孕婦、病人及老人食用。

1 lb. (450 g) .. sea bass
(one whole)
8 .... red jujubes
4 slices aged ginger root
$^1/_4$ C. ...... basil leaves

1 ⌈ 1 t. cooking wine
└ $^1/_2$ t. salt

1　Remove the gills and offal off the fish, wash and cut it widthwise into 2 sections. Wash jujubes and remove the pits.

2　Bring ginger slices, jujubes and 7 C. water to a boil over high heat. Turn the heat to low and simmer until the soup is reduced to 4 C. Add sea bass and cook over medium heat until tender (about 10 minutes). Season with **1** and sprinkle on basil leaves. Serve.

Functions: May reduce cold symptoms like nasal congestion and running nose. Good for pregnant women, patients and the elderly.

髮菜魚片湯 · Black Moss and Fish Soup

魚肉（淨重）................
...... 6 兩（225公克）
豆苗 56公克
胡蘿蔔（淨重）28公克
薑 .... 2 片
高湯 .... 5 杯
髮菜 .... $^1/_4$杯

1
酒 .... 1 小匙
鹽、太白粉各 $^1/_4$小匙
胡椒粉 .... $^1/_8$小匙

2
鹽 .... 1 $^1/_4$小匙
紹興酒、麻油各 1 小匙
胡椒粉、味精 ....
.... 各$^1/_4$小匙

$^1/_2$ lb. (225 g) fish fillet
2 oz. (56 g) .... snow pea leaves
1 oz. (28 g) .... carrot
2 slices .... ginger root
5 C. .... stock
$^1/_4$ C. dried black moss

1
1 t. cooking wine
$^1/_4$ t. each: salt, cornstarch
$^1/_8$ t. pepper

2
1 $^1/_4$ t. salt
1t.each:Shao Hsing rice wine, sesame oil
$^1/_4$ t. pepper

1　魚肉洗淨瀝乾，切4×2公分片狀，入 **1** 料拌醃；髮菜洗淨泡軟瀝乾；豆苗取嫩葉洗淨；胡蘿蔔切4×2公分薄片備用。

2　高湯入鍋煮開，入胡蘿蔔片、薑片、髮菜及魚片再煮開，續入豆苗及**2**料煮開即可。

功效：具有清理內熱，降血脂、血壓，防止壞血病及補充體力之功效。

1　Wash fish fillet and pat dry; cut into 1 $^1/_2$"x $^3/_4$" (4 x 2 cm) slices. Marinate in **1**. Wash black moss. Soak in water until soft; drain. Wash snow pea leaves, trim off the tough parts, only use the tender tips. Cut carrot into 1 $^1/_2$" x $^3/_4$" (4 x 2 cm) thin slices.

2　Bring the stock to a boil, add carrot, ginger slices, black moss and fish. Bring to a boil again. Add snow pea leaves and season with **2**. Bring to a boil and serve.

Functions: May reduce cholesterol and blood pressure. Can improve strength.

魚頭豆腐湯 · Fish Head and Tofu Casserole

鰱魚頭（1個）...............
.... 1斤（600公克）
豆腐（1塊）..................
.... 6兩（225公克）
小豆苗 56公克
薑............................ 6片
鹽........................ $^1/_2$小匙

```
┌ 水 .................... 4杯
│ 酒 ................. 1大匙
1┤ 鹽 ................. 1小匙
└ 胡椒粉 ........ $^1/_8$小匙
```

1 魚頭洗淨，拭乾水份，抹鹽略醃；豆腐分切成8塊；小
   豆苗洗淨，瀝乾備用。

2 鍋熱入油3大匙燒熱，入魚頭煎至兩面呈金黃色，盛起
   瀝油，置砂鍋內，入豆腐、薑片及 1 料煮開，改小火
   加蓋燜煮15分鐘，再入豆苗煮開即可。

   功效：有清利腦目之功效，可治頭風或頭暈且有清熱潤
   燥之作用。

1 $1^1/_3$ lb. (600 g) ..silver
carp head
$^1/_2$ lb. (225 g) ...... tofu
(one block)
2 oz. (56 g) .... baby
pea pod tips
6 slices .... ginger root
$^1/_2$ t. .... salt

```
┌ 4 C. water
│ 1 T. cooking wine
1┤ 1 t. salt
└ $^1/_8$ t. pepper
```

1 Wash the silver carp head and pat dry. Rub with
   salt. Cut the tofu block into 8 pieces. Wash pea
   pod tips and drain.

2 Heat a wok, add 3 T. oil and heat. Fry the fish head
   to brown on both sides; remove and drain off the
   oil. Place the fish head in a casserole, surround it
   with tofu and ginger slices. Pour on 1 and bring to
   a boil. Turn the heat to low, cover with a lid and
   simmer for 15 minutes. Spread the pea pod tips
   on top and bring to a boil. Serve.

   Functions: Improves mental and visual functions.
   Reduces dizzy symptoms and anxiety.

馬蹄海蜇排骨湯 · Jellyfish and Pork Soup

海蜇頭8兩（３００公克）
小排骨6兩（２２５公克）
荸薺 １２顆
薑 .... 4 片

1┌ 鹽、酒 .... 各 $^1/_2$ 大匙
  └ 味精 .... $^1/_4$ 小匙

$^2/_3$ **lb. (300 g) jellyfish**
$^1/_2$ **lb. (225 g) spare ribs**
12 ... water chestnuts
4 slices .... ginger root

1┌ $^1/_2$ **T. each: salt,**
  └ **cooking wine**

1 海蜇頭一片片切開洗淨，泡水２小時以去鹽份（每隔２０分鐘換水一次）；小排骨洗淨，入開水中川燙，隨即撈起，漂涼洗淨；荸薺洗淨，去皮備用。

2 將小排骨、荸薺、薑片及水４杯入燉盅內，加盅蓋入蒸鍋蒸至排骨熟爛（約１小時），再入海蜇頭及**1**料續蒸３分鐘即可。

功效：具有清熱化痰、降血壓之功效。

1 Cut open jellyfish and wash piece by piece. Soak in water for 2 hours to get rid of the salt (change water every 20 minutes). Wash spare ribs and scald in boiling water; remove immediately and rinse under cold water. Wash and pare water chestnuts.

2 Place spare ribs, water chestnuts, ginger slices and 4 C. water into a ceramic steam pot, cover with a lid and steam in a steamer until spare ribs are tender (about 1 hour). Add jellyfish and **1**, continue cooking for 3 more minutes. Serve directly from ceramic pot.

Functions: May reduce inner heat, sputum, and blood pressure.

玉米排骨湯 · Pork and Corn Soup

玉米１２兩（４５０公克）
馬鈴薯８兩（３００公克）
小排骨６兩（２２５公克）

1┌ 鹽 .... 1 $^1/_4$ 小匙
  └ 味精 .... $^1/_4$ 小匙

1 lb. (450 g) .... corn
$^2/_3$ lb. (300 g) potatoes
$^1/_2$ lb. (225 g) spare ribs

1 1 $^1/_4$ t. salt

1 排骨洗淨，入開水中川燙，撈起漂涼洗淨；玉米洗淨，
  切１．５公分寬塊狀；馬鈴薯洗淨去皮，切塊泡水以防
  止變色，煮時再瀝乾水份。

2 鍋內入水８杯煮開，入玉米及排骨煮開，改小火加蓋燜
  煮約１小時，續入馬鈴薯煮至熟軟（約２０分鐘），再
  入**1**料調味即可。

  功效：含有豐富的維他命Ｂ群、Ｃ、Ｅ及鉀質，有
  安神、利尿、降血壓及整腸通便之功效。

1 Wash the ribs and scald in boiling water; remove
  and rinse under cold water. Wash the corn and cut
  into $^5/_8$ " (1.5 cm) sections. Wash the potatoes, peel
  off the skins and cut into serving pieces; soak the
  potato pieces in water to avoid discoloring.

2 Bring 8 C. water to a boil. Add corn and spare ribs,
  bring to a boil. Turn the heat to low, cover with a
  lid and simmer for one hour. Add potatoes and
  simmer until tender (about 20 minutes). Season
  with **1** and serve.

  Functions: Has ample vitamin B complex, C, E
  and potassium. May reduce anxiety, lower blood
  pressure and may improve digestive system.

金針莧菜羹 · Lily Rauden Pottage

莧菜 ... 8兩（３００公克）
干貝、蒜頭 各２粒
高湯 ３杯
金針 １杯

1
┌ 酒 １小匙
│ 鹽 .... ³/₄ 小匙
└ 味精 .... ¹/₈ 小匙

2
┌ 水 ２大匙
└ 太白粉 １¹/₃大匙

$^2/_3$ lb. (300 g)....rauden
2 each: dried scallops,
garlic cloves
3 C. .... stock
1 C. ..dried lily flowers

1
┌ 1 t. cooking wine
└ $^3/_4$ t. salt

2
┌ 2 T. water
└ $1^1/_3$ T. cornstarch

1 金針泡軟洗淨去頭打結；干貝稍沖洗，加水２大匙入蒸
鍋蒸軟，取出撕成細絲，蒸汁留用；莧菜去頭洗淨切３
公分長段；蒜頭洗淨切片備用。

2 鍋熱入油１大匙燒熱，入蒜片爆香，續入高湯及金針煮
開，再依序入莧菜、**1**料、干貝及蒸汁煮開，最後以**2**
料勾芡即可。

功效：含有豐富的鐵質和蛋白質，具有清熱解毒、整腸
開胃、補血明目及預防中暑之功效。

1 Soak dried lily flowers in water until soft, discard
the tough stems. Rinse and tie into knots. Rinse
dried scallops, add 2 T. water and steam until
soft. Remove, leave to cool, then tear to shreds.
Retain the scallop juice for later use. Trim the
ends of rauden, wash and cut into $1^1/_4$" (3 cm)
sections. Wash garlic cloves and slice.

2 Heat a wok, add 1 T. oil and heat. Stir-fry garlic
slices until fragrant. Add stock and lily flowers
and bring to a boil. Add rauden, **1**, scallops, and
juice, bring to a boil. Thicken with **2** and serve.

Functions: Rich in iron and protein. May reduce
inner heat and may have detoxification effect. A
good summer dish for prevention of heat stroke.

香蒡蘿蔔湯 · Gobo Turnip Soup

紫菜 .... ¹/₂張
高湯 .... 8 杯
麻油 .... ¹/₂小匙

1
白蘿蔔（淨重）150公克
胡蘿蔔（淨重）100公克
牛蒡（淨重）56公克
香菇 .... 5 朵

2
鹽 .... ³/₄小匙
味精 .... ¹/₈小匙

¹/₂ .... nori sheet
8 C. .... stock
¹/₂ t. .... sesame oil

1
¹/₃ lb. (150 g) ....
turnip (net weight)
3 ¹/₂ oz. (100 g) ...
carrot (net weight)
2 oz. (56 g) burdock
(net weight)
5 Chinese black
mushrooms

2 ³/₄ t. salt

1 白蘿蔔、胡蘿蔔、牛蒡均切塊；紫菜剪成細絲；香菇
洗淨，加水¹/₂杯泡軟，取出去蒂切半，香菇水備用。

2 鍋入高湯8杯、香菇水及**1**料，以大火煮開改小火，
加蓋燜煮至蘿蔔熟軟（約20分鐘），再加**2**料調味，
淋上麻油並撒上紫菜絲即可。

功效：生津止渴，化痰去滯、助消化，且有抗癌作用。

1 Cut turnip, carrot, and burdock into serving
pieces. Snip nori sheet into fine shreds. Wash
Chinese black mushrooms, soak in ¹/₂ C. warm
water until soft; remove the stems and cut into
halves. Retain the mushroom soaking water for
later use.

2 Bring 8 C. stock, mushroom soaking water, and **1**
to a boil over high heat. Turn the heat to low and
simmer covered until tender (about 20 minutes).
Season with salt, sprinkle on sesame oil and nori
shreds. Serve.

Functions: May reduce thirst and promote saliva.
May improve digestion and acts as an anti-cancer.

番茄豆腐湯 · Tomato and Tofu Soup

番茄8兩（３００公克）
嫩豆腐1塊 ....
...... 8兩（３００公克）
蔥 .... 6 段
蛋 .... 1 個
蔥末 .... 2 大匙
麻油 .... $^1/_2$ 小匙

1┌ 高湯 .... 4 杯
  ├ 鹽 .... 1 小匙
  └ 味精 .... $^1/_4$ 小匙

$^2/_3$ lb. (300 g) tomatoes
$^2/_3$ lb. (300 g) .... soft
tofu (one block)
6 sections green onion
1 .... egg
2 T. minced green onion
$^1/_2$ t. .... sesame oil

1┌ 4 C. stock
   └ 1 t. salt

1 番茄洗淨去蒂，與嫩豆腐均切1公分小丁，蛋去殼打散。

2 鍋熱入油1大匙燒熱，入蔥段爆香，續入番茄丁拌炒數
  下，隨入 **1** 料及豆腐煮開，再徐徐入蛋液煮開後，熄
  火起鍋，撒上麻油及蔥末即可。

功效：含有豐富的維他命C，能增進食慾，活絡胃部機
能，幫助消化平血壓，抗壞血病等功效。

1 Wash the tomatoes and discard the stems. Cut
   both the tomatoes and tofu into $^1/_2$" (1 cm) cubes.
   Beat the egg.

2 Heat a wok, add 1 T. oil and heat. Stir-fry green
   onion sections until fragrant. Add tomato cubes
   to fry, then add **1** and tofu cubes. Bring to a boil.
   Slowly pour in the egg and bring to a boil. Turn off the
   heat and sprinkle on sesame oil and green onion.
   Serve.

   Functions: Rich in vitamin C, improves appetite
   and strengthens digestive system. Can lower blood
   pressure.

銀耳蟹肉羹 · Crab Meat Pottage

蟹1隻8兩（300公克）
雞胸肉 2兩（75公克）
蛋白 1個
高湯 3¹/₂杯
乾白木耳 .... 1 杯
熟青豆仁 .... ³/₄杯
黑醋 .... 1 大匙

1 酒、太白粉各¹/₂小匙
  鹽、胡椒粉各¹/₈小匙

2 洋火腿丁、香菇丁各¹/₄杯
  蔥末 .... 1 大匙
  薑末 .... 1 小匙

3 紹興酒 .... 2 小匙
  鹽 .... 1 ¹/₄小匙
  糖、麻油...... 各¹/₂小匙
  胡椒粉、味精各¹/₄小匙

4 水 .... 2 大匙
  太白粉 .... 1 大匙

$^2/_3$ lb. (300 g)...one crab
2 $^1/_2$ oz. (75 g)...chicken breast
1 .... egg white
3 $^1/_2$ C. .... stock
1 C. .... dried white wood ears
$^3/_4$ C. boiled green peas
1 T. ...... black vinegar

1 $^1/_2$ t. each: cooking wine, cornstarch
  $^1/_8$ t. each: salt, pepper

2 $^1/_4$ C. each: diced ham, diced Chinese black mushrooms
  1 T. minced green onion
  1 t. minced ginger roots

3 2 t. Shao Hsing rice wine
  1 $^1/_4$ t. salt
  $^1/_2$ t. each: sugar, sesame oil
  $^1/_4$ t. pepper

4 2 T. water
  1 T. cornstarch

1 蟹洗淨剝開，去鰓後切半，蟹腳拍裂置盤，入蒸鍋以大火蒸熟（約8分鐘），取出待涼，用筷子或牙籤將肉取出；雞胸肉切小丁，入**1**料拌醃；白木耳泡軟洗淨去蒂切碎備用。

2 鍋熱入油2大匙燒熱，入**2**料炒香，續入高湯煮開，改小火並依序入雞肉、白木耳、蟹肉、**3**料及熟青豆仁煮開，以**4**料勾芡後，再依序入蛋白及黑醋拌勻即可。

■ 活蟹處理的方式為將大螯剪斷，並用筷子插入蟹的內臟，或將蟹直接放入冰箱冷凍，待其斷氣。

功效：具有滋補身體及降火之功效。

1 Wash the crab, split it in two, remove the dregs and then cut the crab body in two. Crack the claws. Steam the crab pieces in a steamer over high heat until done (about 8 minutes). Remove and allow to cool. Remove the crab meat with chopsticks or toothpick. Dice chicken breast and marinate in **1**. Soak dried white wood ears until soft; wash and discard the hard stems, then chop.

2 Heat a wok, add 2 T. oil and heat. Stir-fry **2** until fragrant. Add stock and bring to a boil. Turn the heat to low and add chicken, wood ears, crab meat, **3** and green peas. Bring to a boil and thicken with **4**. Mix in beaten egg white and black vinegar. Serve.

■ If live crab is used, the claws should be snipped off prior to cleaning then pierce crab with chopsticks, or freeze the crab a little while until it stops moving.

Functions: May improve strength and reduce inner heat.

More Wei-Chuan Cook

純青出版社

劃撥帳號：12106299
地址：台北市松江路125號５樓
電話：（02）25084331・25063564
傳真：（02）25074902

Distributor: Wei-Chuan Publishing

1455 Monterey Pass Rd., #110
Monterey Park, CA 91754, U.S.A.
Tel: (213)2613880・2613878
Fax: (213)2613299

健康食譜
- 100道菜
- 120頁
- 中英對照

Healthful Cooking
- 100 recipes
- 120 pages
- Chinese/English Bilingual

素食
- 84道菜
- 120頁
- 中英對照

Vegetarian Cooking
- 84 recipes
- 120 pages
- Chinese/English Bilingual

健康素
- 76道菜
- 96頁
- 中英對照

Simply Vegetarian
- 76 recipes
- 96 pages
- Chinese/English Bilingual

微波食譜第一冊
- 62道菜
- 112頁
- 中英對照

Microwave Cooking Chinese Style
- 62 recipes
- 112 pages
- Chinese/English Bilingual

微波食譜第二冊
- 76道菜
- 128頁
- 中英對照

Microwave Cooking Chinese Style 2
- 76 recipes
- 128 pages
- Chinese/English Bilingual

美味小菜
- 92道菜
- 96頁
- 中英對照

Appetizers
- 92 recipes
- 96 pages
- Chinese/English Bilingual

實用烘焙
- 77道點心
- 96頁
- 中英對照

International Baking Delight
- 77 recipes
- 96 pages
- Chinese/English Bilingual

飲茶食譜
- 88道菜
- 128頁
- 中英對照

Chinese Dim Sum
- 88 recipes
- 128 pages
- Chinese/English Bilingual

養生藥膳
- 73道菜
- 128頁
- 中英對照

Chinese Herb Cooking for Health
- 73 recipes
- 128 pages
- Chinese/English Bilingual

廣東菜
- 75道菜
- 96頁
- 中英對照

Chinese Cuisine Cantonese Style
- 75 recipes
- 96 pages
- Chinese/English Bilingual

Books

家常菜
- 226道菜
- 200頁
- 中文版

營養便當
- 147道菜
- 96頁
- 中文版

嬰幼兒食譜
- 140道菜
- 104頁
- 中文版

米食-家常篇
- 84道菜
- 96頁
- 中英對照

**Rice
Home Cooking**
- 84 recipes
- 96 pages
- Chinese/English Bilingual

米食-傳統篇
- 82道菜
- 96頁
- 中英對照

**Rice
Traditional Cooking**
- 82 recipes
- 96 pages
- Chinese/English Bilingual

麵食-家常篇
- 91道菜
- 96頁
- 中英對照

**Noodles
Home Cooking**
- 91 recipes
- 96 pages
- Chinese/English Bilingual

麵食-精華篇
- 87道菜
- 96頁
- 中英對照

**Noodles
Classical Cooking**
- 87 recipes
- 96 pages
- Chinese/English Bilingual

家常100
- 100道菜
- 96頁
- 中英對照

**Favorite Chinese
Dishes**
- 100 recipes
- 96 pages
- Chinese/English Bilingual

四川菜
- 115道菜
- 96頁
- 中英對照

**Chinese Cuisine
Szechwan Style**
- 115 recipes
- 96 pages
- Chinese/English Bilingual

上海菜
- 91道菜
- 96頁
- 中英對照

**Chinese Cuisine
Shanghai Style**
- 91 recipes
- 96 pages
- Chinese/English Bilingual

台灣菜
- 73道菜
- 120頁
- 中英對照

**Chinese Cuisine
Taiwanese Style**
- 73 recipes
- 120 pages
- Chinese/English Bilingual

庖廚偏方　庖廚錦囊　庖廚樂
- 中文版

味全家政班

味全家政班創立於民國五十年，經過三十餘年的努力，它不只是國內歷史最悠久的家政研習班，更成爲一所正式學制之外的專門學校。

創立之初，味全家政班以教授中國菜及研習烹飪技術爲主，因教學成果良好，備受各界讚譽，乃於民國五十二年，增闢插花、工藝、美容等各門專科，精湛的師資，教學內容的充實，深獲海內外的肯定與好評。

三十餘年來，先後來班參與研習的學員已近二十萬人次，學員的足跡遍及台灣以外，更有許多國外的團體或個人專程抵台，到味全家政班求教，在習得中國菜烹調的精髓後，或返回居住地經營餐飲業，或擔任家政教師，或獲聘爲中國餐廳主廚者大有人在，成就倍受激賞。

近年來，味全家政班亟力研究開發改良中國菜餚，並深入國際間，採集各種精緻、道地美食，除了樹立中華文化「食的精神」外，並將各國烹飪口味去蕪存菁，擷取地方特色。爲了確保這些研究工作更加落實，我們特將這些集合海內外餐飲界與研發單位的經典之作，以縝密的拍攝技巧與專業編輯，出版各式食譜，以做傳承。

薪傳與發揚中國烹飪的藝術，是味全家政班一貫的理念，日後，也將秉持宗旨，永續不輟。

Wei-Chuan Cooking School

Since its establishment in 1961, Wei-Chuan Cooking School has made a continuous commitment toward improving and modernizing the culinary art of cooking and special skills training. As a result, it is the oldest and most successful school of its kind in Taiwan.

In the beginning, Wei-Chuan Cooking School was primarily teaching and researching Chinese cooking techniques. However, due to popular demand, the curriculum was expanded to cover courses in flower arrangements, handcrafts, beauty care, dress making, and many other specialized fields by 1963.

The fact that almost 200,000 students, from Taiwan and other countries all over the world, have matriculated in this school can be directly attributed to the high quality of the teaching staff and the excellent curriculum provided to the students. Many of the graduates have become successful restaurant owners and chefs, and in numerous cases, respected teachers.

While Wei-Chuan Cooking School has always been committed to developing and improving Chinese cuisine, we have recently extended our efforts toward gathering information and researching recipes from different provinces of China. With the same dedication to accuracy and perfection as always, we have begun to publish these authentic regional gourmet recipes for our devoted readers. These new publications will continue to reflect the fine tradition of quality our public has grown to appreciate and expect.